MW00411702

MOTHERS OF THE PROPHETS
SERIES

Lucy Mack Smith

MOTHERS OF THE PROPHETS
SERIES

Lucy Mack Smith

By

Lisa J. Peck

CFI

Springville, Utah

Best wishes,
Lisa J. Peck

ISBN: 1-55517-768-9
e. 1

Published by Cedar Fort Inc.
www.cedarfort.com

Distributed by:

Cover Illustration by Adam Ford
Cover design by Nicole Cunningham
Cover design © 2004 by Lyle Mortimer

Printed in the United States of America
10 9 8 7 6 5 4 3 2 1
Printed on acid-free paper

Library of Congress Cataloging-in-Publication Data

 Peck, Lisa J.
Lucy Mack Smith / by Lisa J. Peck.
p. cm. — (Mothers of the prophets series)
ISBN 1-55517-768-9 (alk. paper)
1. Smith, Lucy, 1775-1856--Fiction. 2. Smith, Joseph, 1805-1844--Family--Fiction. 3. Church of Jesus Christ of Latter-Day Saints--Fiction. 4. Mormon women--Fiction. I. Title. II. Series.
PE1449L83 2004
813'.54--dc22
                                    2004004371

*To Desi—my strong courageous pioneer whose influence
and love will affect generations.*

Forward

In the late fifties a new type of book was created called a "nonfiction novel." This style of book paid careful attention to the historical details of the events and to the real people whose stories they told. Because the books were also novels, the author was offered the freedom to include what the people might have thought, felt, and said. The books in the *Mothers of the Prophets* series fit nicely into this genre. Great care has been taken to ensure the historical accuracy when possible and yet the feelings and thoughts are designed to make the mothers of the prophets feel more real to the reader.

Feeling that Lucy's own expressions are more powerful than any words I could produce, I took the liberty of using Lucy's actual writings when possible, taken from her autobiography *The History of Joseph Smith by His Mother*. These excerpts are in italics throughout the book.

Chapter 1

Here Lies

A worthy matron of unspotted life,
A loving mother, and ... wife,
A friendly neighbor, pitiful to poor,
Whom oft she fed, and clothed with her store ...
And as they did so they reward did find;
A true instructor of her family,
The which she ordered with dexterity;
She public meetings ever did frequent,
And in her closet constant hours she spent;
Religious in all her words and ways,
Preparing still for death, till end of days:
Of all her children, children live to see,
Then dying left a blessed memory.
                                    —Anne Bradstreet, 1643

Personal stories build layer upon layer—developing, growing, expanding our structure, our soul. I have many stories to tell. Some, no doubt, will not believe what I say, will reject my tale as fabrication, a lie, and attribute my story to my blessed ability of imagination. I claim no such gift. Others will be curious listeners, sit for a spell, hear what I have to say, and leave with no apparent change. Still others will wonder if perhaps my story has truth and will search out in their minds, hearts, and souls what for them is truth and what they choose to believe. They will let that truth root in them and my life, my experiences, will intertwine with theirs. While the rare few will take everything I say as truth. Let the curious, the skeptics, and the believers react as they may. As God is my witness, I will tell my experience as it was and worry no more about the effect, for I must write my story.

Why must I write? I must because the *heavens were moved* in my family's and my behalf. *Angels, who had power to put down the mighty from their seats, and to exalt them who were of low degree, were watching over us. I could safely put my trust in Him, as He was able to help in every time of need.* I must praise my Maker by telling the tale of faith, joy, hardship, death, and God's redeeming power.

So I begin.

I was a child of the frontier, a landscape of wilderness and nature springing forth in wild but holy reverence, testifying of its Maker. The area was a rocky region with little land capable of supporting a farm or a garden. Orchards weren't possible. Most of the space became pastures for my family's milk cows, oxen, horses, and beef cattle. On July 8, 1775, in Gilsum, New Hampshire, I came along, the youngest of eight. I held the position of the baby of the family and with my blonde curls and light blue eyes my mother often told me I captured the hearts of many in the small town.

The town was in primitive frontier conditions because the threat of Indians inhibited the settlement of the area. This changed after the French Wars. The first settlers had come in 1763, and had yet to meet the rudimentary requirements to make their land titles good. Despite this, my uncle, Joseph Mack, was commissioned by a proprietor to lay out roads and map homesteads, thus bringing my family to this area—seven children in all with me on the way.

I grew up hearing many comments about the horror of Bunker Hill. The battle had been fought 1,000 miles away. Even so, this event caused my mother great stress as she worried about her infant and her other children and how the war would affect all our lives. My older brother said that I was a good omen because right after my birth George Washington took control of the Revolutionary army. For a while my father bravely served in the war. When he returned, he and my mother were strengths to us children, despite the demands of running a farm and keeping us dressed and fed. My parents had each of us tend to chores. I loved sewing, but disliked churning butter, which seemed to always be my responsibility.

Looking back over my life and the different stages through which I passed, I cannot deny God's firm hand guiding me through this blind existence. I developed a keen interest in the way God nurtured and taught me until my spirituality rose from the dust as a buried spark and grew into a bright flame, becoming the greatest factor in my existence.

My spiritual development came in stages. My father, Solomon Mack, had a strong influence on me in the beginning, particularly as I took after him in my complacency toward Godly matters. Let me tell you more about his background to better understand.

My father's grandfather, John Mack (1682-1734), was a prosperous trader in Lyme, Connecticut. He gave land to my grandpa, Ebenezer Mack, for an inheritance. Father was born on this land on September 15, 1732. Times grew hard for my grandfather as economic struggles swept across the new country. To my grandfather's great sorrow and despite all his desparate attempts to save his inherited land, he was unable to do so. This resulted in the heart-breaking decision to send my uncle and aunt into indentured households so they could survive. My grandparents also had to send my father away at the tender age of four into particularly bad conditions. My father was beaten, underfed, and treated as another slave on the plantation. He was unable to rise above this condition until he reached the age of twenty-one. This powerfully affected his mindset to the point that he was consumed with thoughts of survival and wealth.

Later, when Father reached an elderly age and experienced a change of heart, he realized that serving under such a master caused him to grow up feeling like a wild animal without respect for society.[1] My father tried to become great by pursuing money.[2] As a result, he became a largely absent member of our family. Instead of being home he pursued one venture after another. He survived a tree falling on him, spills from horses, becoming permanently lame, a shipwreck, and betrayal by business associates. Although there were times when events would change our situation, for the most part Father did not do too badly in a worldly sense. He was determined to "lay up treasures in this world."[3] Over the years, Father owned a variety of houses and farms. He also accumulated enough resources to buy land, freight vessels, and a schooner. He even had enough extra to lend a few people one hundred dollars. I admired him and saw no folly in his extreme ambition to better our situation. Acquiring money has become his religion. Despite this fact, religion in my childhood home was practiced through prayer and the singing of hymns at my mother's insistence.

My mother, Lydia Gates Mack, a native of East Haddam, Connecticut, was the daughter of a deacon in the Congregational Church. She did not subscribe to that church or any other formal church, but did have a very pious allegiance to God. She encouraged me to worship God with my whole being. However, I yielded more to Father's lack of belief in a great Maker. I had very few feelings, if any, to make me heaven bound.

From these conditions in which God placed me, I now understand the events of my childhood served a divine purpose. I do not know, and doubt I will ever completely grasp in this mortal existence, how those early years in a harsh situation taught me skills I would need later in life.

It seemed that my childhood was riddled with one sore trial after another. When I was three, Father was carried home half-dead by other men. He had been struck by a falling tree, which crushed him "almost all to pieces."[4] I have little recollection of this event, except a few gasps from Mother and having an overwhelming impression that something was dreadfully wrong, hearing whispers and painful whimpers from Father and seeing the wrinkled brows of visitors.

Father lay on his back in bed unable to move for two months. When he was capable of moving, he was forced to conform to continued bed rest for another two months. But Father wasn't one to lie still. The moment enough strength returned to him, he struggled to the sawmill where he did millwork to help an employee with broken machinery, using crutches for mobility. Father's balance must have been wobbly because he returned to our house an awful sight, reporting that he had fallen "on the waterwheel bruising himself most horribly."[5]

Watching Father, the man my world revolved around, continually suffering dangerous blows and beset with such dreadful accidents, caused me to be consumed with fear whenever he left my sight. I clung to him when he was recovered enough to tolerate me wrapping my arms around his strong legs, and cried when he ventured out on other tasks. I felt there was no way of preventing the awful calamities from happening to him. He seemed to have provoked nature.

My fears once again were realized when Father could manage walking. This time he was injured when a tree branch fell on his head. This accident caused Father to be stricken with "fits" periodically for the rest of his life. When a spell would come over him, shaking him from head to toe, my whole frame would freeze in fear. I dared not breathe as I watched him, listening for his lungs to catch and maintain breath. During some of these episodes, he would fall unconscious.

The worst fit I remember happened when Father was determined to go to work on his own. He was traveling along the hills in the countryside when one of those brutal seizures came upon him. The "face of the land was covered with ice" when Father said he was knocked "senseless from 1 p.m. until 5 p.m." When he woke, he found himself "all covered with blood and much cut and bruised."[6]

These fits wouldn't overtake Father often, actually quite rarely, but when they did, fear shot straight through our home. I remember more than one time stumbling onto Mother crying when she thought we were away doing our chores. Constant worry caused me to cling, but other times I must have wanted to protect myself from the pain of getting too close to someone who would soon be gone, so I would distance myself from Father. It turned out that I would not lose Father for years, and even then his passing had nothing to do with his fits or any other terrible accident.

For the next four years, Father became a privateer with two of my brothers. While serving in his fishing schooner and freighters, he encountered battles on the sea. With pride he passionately recounted these stories when he was at home. He had been successful in capturing eight British vessels along Long Island in 1779. For accomplishing this feat, he received prize money. Not only did he often mention the fact that the fight had merited prize money, but also that the feat was so stunning that it landed in the newspapers in the home port of New London.

After hearing at great length how his life hung like a thread dangling over an open flame, I determined that fate would soon catch up with Father and I would lose him. When I was eight years old, it seemed clear this would happen when he announced he was launching off on a great adventure for Nova Scotia with my oldest brother, Jason. Father, then called "Old Captain Mack," explained to me that he would soon return and that the trip was necessary because "a heavy debt that had been due [him] for a long time was collected and ready" for him.[7] He had received a letter from Liverpool[8] explaining that the funds awaited him. The trip was to take three months. I sat on his lap listening, tears escaping me.

"A brief time," he said, kissing my forehead. "Then I will be back with you again."

At this point, my brother was a "preacher of the gospel" and he believed "that by prayer and faith, the gifts of the gospel, which were enjoyed by the ancient disciples of Christ, might be attained." Not only had my brother "labored almost incessantly to convert others to the same faith," he also had developed strong feelings for Esther, a young woman of his acquaintance who was of "wealthy parentage."

To my sadness and to Esther's, who was now Jason's fiancée, Father convinced my brother to take the trip with him. Although I was young at the time, I could not help thinking of how hard it must have been for Esther to be separated from the man she loved who was far away on the great blue sea. I perhaps would have dwelled on this situation much longer if tragedy hadn't unfolded within our home.

My dear mother came down ill with a severe sickness. This, of course, caused me great worry with Father at sea and Mother laid up in her bed, growing worse. I wondered if I would be sent off to be an indentured servant if Mother passed away. I feared I would perhaps never see Father or any of my siblings again. My thoughts became carried away as the grief of seeing Mother in such a condition pressed on me. Maybe it was my age, but another part of me felt sure Mother would grow well soon. However, this hope was shattered when her friends came to visit and left in tears, shaking their heads.

I would not allow myself to see what was happening until one morning when my brothers and sisters and I were called around Mother's bed. She lay there, face pale with blotches from the fever, weak, and struggling to gesture to me to come closer. She held my hand and gazed at me straight in the eyes. "Lucy, please remember what I taught you. Remember to *fear God and walk uprightly before him.*"

Still holding my hand, she gestured to my older brother, Stephen. "Stephen, I don't believe I will make it through this fever much longer. Please take Lucy under your protection and raise her as I would and as though she were your own child."

"I will, Mother. Do not let that worry you."

To our surprise, Mother's life did not fall into the hands of Death, but instead she made a dramatic turn for the better and rapidly recovered. This was a great relief to my young soul, after coming so near to losing Mother and her tenderness, her love, and the compassion that I so needed.

Seeing my brother Stephen so willing to take me as his own, I felt something more than what he said in those interchanges with my mother. I knew with a deep knowing that my brother loved me and he considered me as one of his own. This bond and connection was never broken throughout our lifetimes.

Our relief at Mother's recovery was not to be enjoyed for long. A creditor went to great lengths to cheat Mother, which left us in such a depressed state that we were evicted from our home without any money to our names.

Mother's strength held us together through this trial. She bore it with remarkable courage and valor, which I remembered later when it was my turn to lead my children. I marveled at the way she held up under such situations. Her focus, her concerns, were always on her children. She nurtured us and called down the mercies from the Father above to provide for us.

As we suffered without a home, another blow came that nearly shattered our resolve. We received word that Father and my oldest brother, Jason, had died at sea. This news came from my brother's fiancée, Esther. Each time she went to speak of it the dear girl was overcome with grief. She had received letters reporting Jason's passing. This brought a black blanket upon us that refused to be lifted.

Two years passed with this grief a constant reminder in our hearts. Eventually, Esther accepted that her true love was lost to her forever and married a man who had been seeking her hand almost from the beginning of Jason's departure. One can imagine Esther's complete shock, as well as ours, when Father and Jason returned four months after her wedding, with tales of surviving horrific conditions.

Jason's former love was returning from her brother's funeral when she laid eyes on him. She collapsed. It was soon known that Esther's husband, who had worked at the post office, had withheld Jason's heart-felt letters to her and had forged the letter telling of Jason's death. He pretended to be Jason's friend and wrote of his untimely death so relatives back home would no longer expect him. All this was done in order to win Esther's hand in marriage. Esther's health quickly gave out, and she lingered for the space of two years before she passed from this earth.

Watching my brother's heartache, his dear love die, and the death of the romance that should have bloomed to full fruition—all because of the deceptions of one man—was hard for me to bear as a child. I cried often over the sadness of the situation.

I was also horrified to hear Father's tales of what he and my brother encountered while they were away from us. Their journey started with fishing voyages off Nova Scotia when "a terrible hurricane as [he] had ever [seen] in [his] life"[9] came upon them. The storm was so dreadfully frightful that everyone fled from the vessel except Father and Jason. They bravely weathered out the storm in an attempt to save the ship. After they recovered from that adventure, they "took in a freight of dry goods" [10] at Halifax, and headed westward around Nova Scotia for Horton. Misfortune followed them, for the ship became stuck on reefs. They had to solicit help from smaller vessels to carry their load into the Liverpool harbor.

Father participated in other schemes to increase his wealth. Having lost a lot of his money, he was determined not to return home without collecting a profit. This wore greatly on Jason, not wanting to be away from his beloved any longer. He insisted that Father go home. Almost home, Father fell ill for weeks in Salem. Jason accepted his fate, patiently keeping his mind and thoughts on the glorious, long-overdue reunion that he was to enjoy with his fiancée. Unfortunately, it was never to be.

All told, Father and Jason had been gone four years, from 1784 to 1788. Upon their return, they found that in addition to Jason losing his true love, the family had lost home and finances. This sad turn of events would haunt me for many years to come, causing me to question God, asking why a God would allow such a thing to happen to such good souls as my brother and his fiancée.

Chapter 2

God wasn't done carving out my character in my childhood. The next challenges were perhaps some of the hardest I had to bear and brought me to one of the biggest crossroads of my life. In 1782, my older sister, Lovisa, fell ill with consumption. This happened two years after her marriage to Joseph Tuttle. At this point they had not been able to have a child, which disappointed me since I wanted a nephew or a niece, myself being the youngest of eight. I had an extreme desire to be a motherly figure to someone and dote on a child as I had been doted upon.

The illness had consumed Lovisa's reserves to the point that my other older sister, Lovina, was called in to aid her and her husband. As the consumption progressed through the years, I was called in to help too, which I did gladly.

Consumption is a frightful, wasting disease that comes in waves. While I was with my sister, she grew extremely ill. I did not know how she could continue to live. Yet after I had given up and determined all was lost, she regained her strength. At times it seemed as though she had recovered only to fall ill again, in worse condition than before.

After two years of battling with consumption, Lovisa showed signs that she would return to full health. We became hopeful for a complete recovery, but soon the illness came upon her violently. This *re-attack brought her down again, and she grew worse and worse, until she became entirely speechless, and so reduced that her attendants were not allowed to even turn her in bed. She took no nourishment except a very little rice water. She lay in this situation three days and two nights. On the third night, about two o'clock, she feebly pronounced the name of Lovina, who had all the while watched over her pillow, like an attendant angel, observing every change and symptom with the deepest emotion.*

My sister, Lovina, cried, *"My sister! My sister! What will you?"*

Then to the shock of all who heard the story, Lovisa said, *"The Lord has healed me, both soul and body—raise me up and give me my clothes, I wish to get up."*

What took place after this I have often contemplated. My sisters at that time joined together in prayer and song to glorify God. The miracle that next unfolded shouldn't come as a surprise to a believer, but for me, who never thought too deeply about God or His existence, the unfolding events stirred a spiritual awakening, proving that I was truly witnessing the power of the All Mighty who came down from the heavens above and reached out to our family to administer in our behalf.

Lovisa, who had been on her deathbed, asked for assistance with dressing and standing up. Her husband went along with her requests, thinking her behavior was a revival before her death.

All eyes watched Lovisa with amazement and anxiety, thinking that at any moment she would slump over in death. But instead of dying, as all expected, she requested to be taken to her father–in–law who also was in bed suffering from illness. Not wanting to argue with a dying woman, we escorted her to her father-in-law's bedside.

My frail, pale sister made her way carefully to his side and placed her slender hand upon his arm. *"God has raised me up, and I have come to tell you to prepare for death."*

This story spread rapidly through the town and it was not long before Lovisa was asked to speak at church on Sunday. At the beginning of the meeting the preacher said, *"Many of the congregation have doubtless come to hear a recital of the strange circumstances which have taken place in the neighborhood, and as [I] [feel] more interested in it than in hearing a gospel discourse, [I] [will] open the meeting and then give place to Mrs. Tuttle."*

When my sister took the pulpit, she spoke in a clear, strong voice, so different from the day before when she was breathing her last breaths. She said, *"I seemed to be borne away to the world of spirits, where I saw the Savior, as through a veil, which appeared to me about as thick as a spider's web, and he told me that I must return again to warn the people to prepare for death; that I must exhort them to be watchful as well as prayerful; that I must declare faithfully unto them their accountability before God, and the certainty of their being called to stand before the judgment seat of Christ; and that if I would do this, my life should be prolonged."*

This happy event brought mixed emotions because before this, Lovina had started coughing. Her ailment eventually developed into consumption as well. This caused my family great worry as both of my sisters struggled with the life-threatening illness for years. By the time I was sixteen years old I had reached the age and the strength to be able to *carry my twenty-nine-year-old sister from chair to bed.*

Finally it happened. Even though Lovisa's life had been prolonged, the grasp of death came for her three years later. Much stressed about her condition and hoping beyond hope that somehow she would pull out of this brush with death again, as had happened so often in my family, *I never allowed myself to go an hour at a time, beyond the sound of her voice while she was sick.*

In the middle of the night, Lovisa breathed out the request that I dreaded. *"Lucy, please call for Father and Mother, for I wish to see them, as I would soon be gone."*

After speaking words of faith and warning to us, she next focused on what was happening to her with a smile. She held up her hand weakly and said, *"See, the blood is settling under my nails."* She crossed her hands and said, *"'Tis cold to there—soon this mortal flesh will be food for worms."*

I gasped, not believing how calm and horrifically she spoke, but she seemed to pay that no mind and turned to me and said, *"Now, sister Lucy, will you help me into bed?"*

Despite feeling like I was being swallowed up into a great pit of despair, I picked her up as I would a child. Her condition and frame had deteriorated to the point that I was able to carry her without struggle.

I cannot forget what happened next as it plays out in my mind like a continued waking nightmare. *As I was carrying her to bed, my hand slipped. At this she cried out, "Oh! Sister, that hurt me." This, indeed, gave me bitter feelings, I was well assured, that this was the last sad office I should ever perform for my sister, and the thought that I had caused her pain in laying her on her death bed, wounded me much.*

All this talk of God and His goodness and my sister's warning about preparing to meet Him caused a great unrest to stir within me. I struggled to believe in a God who would take my sister away from me. Then I would be filled with huge waves of guilt for not feeling more grateful for the three extra years we had been blessed to have her.

The huge blackness that pressed on me from losing someone who I loved so much was not the only trial I faced. Soon after my sister passed away, my other sister, Lovina, took a turn for the worst. I was called to nurse her at her bedside. As I nursed my sister as tenderly as I could, I could not help but remember almost hourly how I had hurt Lovisa in her last passing moments. I lived in fear that I would cause pain again. I took much care in transporting Lovina from chair to bed and back again. I forced myself to focus on the task at hand.

At last a letter was sent to my father asking for his assistance, believing that Lovina would not continue in this life. Lovina wanted to return to her childhood home despite all hazards. It took much persuasion for my father to consent to taking her on this trip. Eventually he agreed. They had made it about four miles to Gilsum when the father and daughter came across an inn. Father, thinking it wise to allow Lovina to rest a bit to regain her strength, stopped at the inn and put Lovina in a chair for a much needed rest. He then sought water for her tired limbs. Upon returning to his daughter's side, he found that she, too, had escaped the trappings of this life and her spirit had soared heavenward.

The deaths of my two older sisters, within one year, were a blow that I was not able to handle with much grace. I found the overwhelming heaviness and sadness of it extremely difficult to bear. Both sisters had talked about meeting their Maker, a being of whom I had no strong convictions, but who had filled my soul with torment. How could He allow such hardships in this life?

I felt I was losing my family. Many were the times I had imagined my father and brother dead when they were at sea, and also when death kept knocking on my father's door in the form of a multitude of accidents. I trusted that persistent Death would eventually succeed in taking my father from me. Death had gone after my mother and though she had won that battle, we had lost our money and our home.

As the reality of the passing of my sisters sank deeper in my soul, melancholy overtook me. Despite all that had befallen our family, there was one sibling besides myself who did not seem to have as much hard luck befall him. This was my older brother Stephen, who, when Mother was about to pass from this world, had agreed to take me in his home as one of his own.

In Detroit he was a Major who merchandised *upon quite an extensive scale. He did considerable other public work, for the purpose of giving employment to the poor.* Stephen was also a soldier in the Revolutionary War, along with Father. He faced death as he fought in many battles on land and sea and encountered a famine during his time of service. When circumstances such as these arose, he handled them by realizing that *his entire dependence upon God, the hand of Providence was always manifested in his deliverance.*

It was after the death of my two dear sisters that Stephen requested I visit him. He had heard of the overwhelming grief I was burdened with and thought a visit would do me good. I agreed to the trip and traveled eighty miles north of Gilsum to Tunbridge, Vermont. During this trip and my stay with my brother, I wrestled with the issues of religion. I needed God, and I needed to believe my sisters weren't gone forever. Thus, through a host of childhood traumas— illness, death, the threat of losing loved ones at every turn, watching my brother's heartbreak through deception, losing homes and struggling with money—I came to the end of tolerance and an end to complacency. I actively sought a more enriched spiritual life. My sisters' deathbed testimonies had a powerful effect on me. I realized I did believe in God. I actively pursued religion at this time, seeking for the proper way to worship Him.

As I was propelled onto this religious journey, I soon confronted a problem. *If I remain a member of no church, all religious people will say I am of the world, and if I join some one of the different denominations, all the rest will say I am in error.* I spent many hours going over this problem with Stephen and finally, after much prayer and investigation of different churches, I concluded that I'd seek my solace and worship God through Bible reading and prayer.

When I finally embraced the truth of God's existence, a belief which I feel I must have always known but had not kept at the forefront of my mind, my life took another surprising twist. It was as though God said, "At last, Lucy, you realize your need for me, now let's see what you do with this."

It was after I embraced God that a handsome young man came into my life. He was a tall, intelligent, athletic man who loved to wrestle and had the reputation of being able to subdue two men at once. He had his own ideas and spoke them freely to anyone who would listen. He had a profound faith in a personal God and Savior, but refused to have anything to do with denominations because he could not reconcile the teachings of the churches with scriptures and his own reasoning. These qualities drew me to him.

He had endured hardships. When he was young, he had suffered a burn which injured the cords of his neck. The damage made one of his strong broad shoulders higher than the other. This injury was not overlooked by passers-by who made rude remarks. He earned the name "Crook Neck," which he was proud to be called. This man, who happened to be a neighbor to my brother, Stephen, came to call on me early in my stay in Tunbridge. His name was Joseph Smith. His visits to my brother's house became more frequent until none of us could deny that he was courting me. I much looked forward to seeing him and to the laughter we enjoyed as he discussed with much seriousness his beliefs and ideas about life. I felt the heavens had opened and showered joy on me in drenching proportions. I was much taken by him and felt this happiness would continue forever if I were with him.

I was twenty-two years old when I married this handsome, strong man in 1797. What were my feelings as I held his hand during the marriage ceremony? Truly, I had none. I knew marrying him was right. I knew he was a good man. Therefore, I married him. It was that simple.

Chapter 3

$\mathcal{S}$ tanding by Joseph's side for all our years together brought a deep-rooted happiness to my life. Often I would set out of my home for a breath of air to watch the sunset and I would see Joseph working near the barn. This let me know that no matter what we faced, we stood together, supporting and loving each other. This gave us hope and the strength to continue on. At times when pressures threatened to overwhelm us, Joseph would pull me close to him in a strong embrace. As I nestled against him, resting my head on his chest, hearing the sound of his heartbeat, love would pour from him, letting me feel safe, cared for, and comforted. It was as though God's love flowed through him to me. I treasure those moments, those glimpses of eternity.

Children started coming to us early. Within the first year of our marriage a beautiful boy arrived. Words cannot express how overwhelmed and awed I was by the miracle of his life. I held that sweet spirit close to my chest, letting my child know of his magnificence. My joy lasted for a few brief days, then my baby's life was snatched away from me. When this happened, I greatly desired to retreat from living, like I had done when my sisters passed away. Then

I wondered if my sisters had greeted my son. The idea of my sisters taking care of my baby until I could be with him again was comforting and gave me the strength to carry on.

A year later we moved to Vermont and another boy came. To my great happiness this son lived, his name Alvin. Two years later, in 1800, Hyrum arrived. Another three years passed before our first girl, Sophronia, blessed us with her presence.

Over the years I have reflected much about the turn of events and how they have affected me eternally. I realize God has a hand in all aspects of our lives. I wish I could say I was more faithful than most of humanity, that I always remembered and believed in God, and that He was a noticeably active deity in my life, but if I wrote that, I would be lying. I was fortunate enough to be surrounded by people who believed. One of the testimonies that affected me most, and sunk deep into my soul, was that of my older sister, Lovisa. When she had seemingly died and saw God on the other side of the veil, and then returned declaring that we needed to repent and that death wasn't far away, her words changed my way of thinking. Through the years her message, and the energy she put into it as she shared it with everyone who'd listen, haunted me and I drew upon it in 1803, at age 28, when my spirituality reached its crossroads.

During this year I came down with a cold, which was not unusual, but instead of recovering after a week or two, the cold intensified and transformed into a fever. I also had a cough, which I had taken every effort to cure. These symptoms worried me, since they had a striking resemblance to the illness that had taken my sisters.

I grew sicker and struggled as much as I could to keep the house running. Sometimes when I was too weak to get out of bed, my younger children would lay next to me. Finally I was diagnosed with what I dreaded and knew I had—consumption. I was plagued by worries of leaving my young children motherless, and departing from a husband who, despite his inability to admit it openly, needed me. All these things pressed on me. But the heaviest weight was that I knew I was unprepared to meet God.

I believed in God and yet He had not been a standard or an ensign in my life. My mother had done her best to teach me the principles contained in the Bible, but I hadn't invested sufficient effort in preparing to meet my Maker. I felt as though there was *a dark and lonesome chasm, between myself and the Savior, which I dared not attempt to pass.*

As I lay in bed coughing, drenched with perspiration, I wrestled with my deathly fear of meeting my Maker unprepared. Like an angel, my mother nursed me and saw to it that my household ran smoothly. I knew I drew dangerously close to my death when my mother could no longer hide her fear when she looked at me. Then my husband rushed to my side. *"Oh, Lucy! my wife! my wife! you must die! The doctors have given you up; and all say you cannot live."*

The desperation was so great that I turned to where my mother had taught me. *I looked to the Lord, and begged and pleaded with him to spare my life, in order that I might bring up my children, and be a comfort to my husband. My mind was much agitated during the whole night. Sometimes I contemplated heaven and heavenly things; then my thoughts would turn upon those of earth—my babies and my companion.*

During this night I made a solemn covenant with God, that, if he would let me live, I would endeavor to serve him according to the best of my abilities.

Shortly after this, I heard a voice say to me, "Seek, and ye shall find; knock, and it shall be opened unto you. Let your heart be comforted; ye believe in God, believe also in me."

In a few moments my mother came in, and, looking upon me she said, "Lucy, you are better."

I replied, as my speech returned just at that instant, "Yes, mother, the Lord will let me live, if I am faithful to the promise which I made to him, to be a comfort to my mother, my husband, and my children." I continued to gain strength, until I became quite well as to my bodily health; but my mind was considerably disquieted. It was wholly occupied upon the subject of religion. As soon as I was able, I made all diligence in endeavoring to find someone who was capable of instructing me more perfectly in the way of life and salvation.

This experience and blessing from God set me on a search that lasted for many years, but it was also my rebirth. I was alive in Christ, and as I studied the Bible and attended various church meetings, I grew closer to my Creator. From that point on, I made a conscious effort to seek His will and push mine aside. I also sought with great diligence to teach my children about God.

My greatest frustration was in trying to find a church that resembled the spirit I had felt on my deathbed. I was saddened that I could not find a church that accurately represented my experience with God and the principles I found in the Bible. In order to try to fulfill my promise to God and continue in my worship of Him, I determined to study the Bible and the teachings found there and to apply the principles illustrated in my own life. I would not allow organized religion to take away the knowledge I had received from Him. I put my trust in my Lord. I believed with all my heart that He would guide me spiritually, and when the time came I would find what I sought, or if I did not find it, that by living by His words, I would have earned the right to have my Heavenly Father pleased in me. It struck me as interesting that as I continued down this path, looking into different churches and finding that they did not match my interpretation of the Bible or the spirit that I had felt directly from God on my deathbed, I did not feel compelled to get baptized until years later.

When the compulsion to get baptized came to me, I had a strong burning in my chest. I wanted to follow the principles Christ taught. If he, being the God of all, saw that it was important for himself to be baptized by immersion, I also saw that I, a sinner, had a great need to follow suit. It took time to find a preacher who would baptize me without my declaring membership in his church. But at last, after seventeen years, the good Lord guided me to a preacher who was willing to grant my heart's desire. I was baptized in 1820 in Palmyra. The willing preacher was a Presbyterian.

When I was pulled from the water, I felt a great pressure fall off my chest. I also experienced a deep sadness as I thought about my husband who, although a very good man, refused to participate in any church, and who most definitely refused to be baptized. He would have nothing to do with organized religion. He felt that all of it was greatly in error.

Concerned over the situation of my husband's lack of interest in religion, I retreated into a grove of trees near our home to plead with the Lord for my husband. After much wrestling with the spirit, I asked *that the true gospel might be presented to him, and that his heart might be softened so as to receive it, or, that he might become more religiously inclined.* I spent a long time in my prayers without an answer. Depressed, I went to sleep that night and dreamed a dream that revealed to me the message to not worry any more on the subject. The dream showed me that when my husband Joseph *was more advanced in life, he would hear and receive with his whole heart, and rejoice therein; and unto him would be added intelligence, happiness, glory, and everlasting life.* Soon after this revelation, my husband had significant dreams that would prepare him for what was to come.

*

Chapter 4

God decided to test, mold, and enhance my character through the trials of moving, sickness, the loss of loved ones, and my longing to be near my family. He also expanded my capabilities through another type of challenge. He did not leave me stranded, though, for He prepared me to survive through the next struggle many years before it came upon me and my husband.

As is often the case in God's dealings with His people, His help came through another individual. This happened to be my good brother Stephen. He, as I have mentioned earlier, did well pertaining to the things of this world, and upon having such a blessing in his life, decided that when I married he would give me a very generous wedding present of one thousand dollars. I had stored the money away in hopes of doing up a home. Little did I know that years later I would be eternally grateful to my brother for such generosity and for my prudence of reserving it for the future.

Years after receiving his generous gift, I was living in Randolph, having moved from Tunbridge where I lived with my husband and three children. We decided to rent our farmhouse and move to a larger village to allow us the opportunity to run a store.

We felt the hand of the Lord and recognized that He was blessing us. But we also thought that perhaps we could earn more profit to better our living standard. This line of thought grew when Joseph happened to learn he could make an enormous profit by freighting ginseng root to China.

Ginseng was in high demand among the people of China because of their belief in the power of the herb, which was said to be a remedy for many things, including impotence. It was also purported to prolong life, and it was heralded for its restorative abilities. But the biggest reason this herb was sought after was because of its healing powers against the plague that raged in China.

Joseph strove to gather as much of the root as possible. He traded and collected it. After he had retrieved enough, he made sure the root crystallized before taking it to New York where he planned to organize a business transaction. With this in mind, he ran into a Mr. Stevens from Royal, New York, who offered him $3,000 for his ginseng. However, we stood to make $4,500 if we sold the ginseng to China. Joseph opted for the larger portion of money. He put our ginseng on consignment to ship to China with a certain captain of a ship. They formed a written obligation.

Joseph was so confident we would receive the money back, and that we had finally pulled ourselves out of poverty, that he risked all the money that would normally have gone toward supplies in our store to pay for the root. He put all the extra money we had into this pursuit, placed the goods on credit, and anxiously awaited the return of Mr. Stevens.

Time dragged, and no word came. Finally my husband set off to find out the situation. Later we learned that when Mr. Stevens caught word that my husband had put the ginseng on a ship, he hurriedly traveled back to New York to find the ship and have his son board as

a passenger. He brought his own ginseng and convinced the captain
to let his son handle both transactions.

When we learned that the son of Mr. Stevens was back from
China, my husband immediately sought him out. The younger Mr.
Stevens looked solemn when he said the sale he had tried to secure
had failed and the only thing he was able to get for us was a small
chest of tea.

Joseph was greatly agitated over this whole situation, realizing
that his failure to gain profit with the ginseng had put all our assets
at risk if he did not come up with other funds quickly. He was also
very suspicious of the younger Mr. Stevens and the truthfulness of his
tale. The suspicion grew when the young man hired ten people to
help him with the work of crystallizing ginseng. Soon after the young
Mr. Stevens had his business working, my brother decided to see what
he could find out by visiting him. Mr. Stevens had a liking of alcohol
and he was taken by spirits when my brother happened in.

My brother talked to the young Mr. Stevens and said, *"Well, Mr.
Stevens, you are doing a fine business; you will soon be ready for another trip
to China."*

And then again. *"Oh, Mr. Stevens, how much did Brother Smith's
adventure bring?" Being under the influence of liquor, he was not on his
guard, and took my brother by the hand and led him to a trunk; then opening
it, he observed, "There, sir, are the proceeds of Mr. Smith's ginseng!" exhibiting
a large amount of silver and gold.*

My faithful brother rushed to my husband to reveal the truth.
Immediately Joseph took measures to go after this young thief, and I
engaged in prayers that we would be successful in retrieving what was
rightfully ours. Both our attempts failed.

When Mr. Stevens emerged out of his intoxication, he reflected on what he had done. Soon after, he let his new employees go, gathered all the money and headed for Canada.

My husband spent a great amount of time in pursuit of Mr. Stevens. Joseph finally came home after a long trip spent searching for him. I placed my hand on his chest and gently said, "Joseph, it is no use. He is gone and you need to let him go and direct your focus on other things." This calmed Joseph. He was a reasonable man and husband and he recognized that what I said was true.

Our creditors heard of the tale and were nervous about getting paid. They came after us for the funds. My husband and I sat holding hands one solemn day to see where we stood in relation to money and the world. The outcome was grim indeed. *He discovered that, in addition to the loss sustained by the China adventure, he had lost about two thousand dollars in bad debts. At the time he sent his venture to China he was owing eighteen hundred dollars in the city of Boston for store goods.* Because he had put all his faith into the ginseng, we had nothing to pay these obligations. *The principal dependence left him, in the shape of property, was the farm at Tunbridge, upon which we were then living, having moved back to this place immediately after his venture was sent to China. This farm, which was worth about fifteen hundred dollars, my husband sold for eight hundred dollars, in order to make a speedy payment on the Boston debt; and, as I had not used the check of one thousand dollars, which my brother and Mr. Mudget gave me, I added it to the eight hundred dollars obtained from the sale of the farm.*

Chapter 5

I felt fortunate that children came to Joseph and I so easy and so many. I was blessed with delightful spirits that it was a privilege to help cultivate and raise. Joseph Jr. was born in 1805, Samuel H. in 1808, my precious Ephraim, who died eleven days after his birth in 1810, William in 1811, Catherine in 1813, Don Carlos in 1816 and our last and eleventh child, Lucy, was born in 1824. As the children came, God continued to chisel my character. I was to discover, as all naïve young people do, that my trials had only begun. What troubles I endured as a child were merely preparation for what lay in store for me as an adult. One of the greatest tests that I faced, and what helped deepen my spirituality, came when typhus fever hit our town of Lebanon, New Hampshire. This deadly disease had been sweeping the country with a tremendous force.

My son Hyrum came home from the academy at Hanover and brought the illness with him. He was the first one stricken, but was not the last by far. One by one, all of our seven children contracted this killing disease. My child would come down with a boiling-hot fever that brought chills and weakness along with it. As I struggled to gain control of the fever, the headaches, rashes, and sometimes delirium, my older children quietly took over the household tasks. I tried not to worry when my child's skin became mottled and their tongue black, but I knew these signs too well. The stress wore on the family as we labored diligently to take care of our ailing children. We offered many prayers, petitioning the Lord for help.

At age ten, my dear daughter Sophronia had a dreadful time with the illness. It was like I was in a fog for three months. Doctors came over every day and every day I wondered if she was going to live. On the ninetieth day the doctors declared, "Sophronia will die. There's nothing else that can be done."

"There *are* things we can do for her," I said to the doctor, "but I do appreciate all your efforts in trying to save my daughter." I had no intention of taking his word as final. I thanked him and escorted him to the front door. Once he was gone, I turned to my husband and we immediately sank to our knees. We continued to pray together for an extended amount of time, pouring *out our grief to God, in prayer and supplication, beseeching him to spare our child yet a little longer.*

After the prayers, I looked at my daughter's young face and saw her remain motionless with her eyes fixed as if in death. I continued to gaze at her *as a mother looks upon the last shade of life in a darling child.* I would not reconcile myself to this. I had a strong impression that my daughter would live and I would not give her up into the arms of Death without a fight.

I grabbed a blanket and wrapped it around Sophronia, then carried her around the room, holding her as close to me as I possibly could. When I had done this, it appeared to all that my daughter had stopped breathing and her spirit had left her body. People in the room commented on my odd behavior. *"Mrs. Smith, it is all of no use; you are certainly crazy, your child is dead."*

Nowithstanding, I would not, for a moment, relinquish the hope of again seeing her breathe and live. At their protests, I held my daughter closer to my chest, praying in my mind and exercising my faith that my child would live. My reaction hushed everyone in the room; all eyes remained fixed upon me. I had been promised by God that Sophronia would live, and I would not give up my efforts to bring her back with love and faith.

The room became ghastly quiet as all continued to watch me, most probably filled with sympathy that my grief over my lost child had driven me to madness. But *I could not at this trying moment deny that God had power to save to the uttermost all who call on him.* My whole soul, heart, and mind called upon His grace and mercy and would not stop until my plea was heard. All the doubts of the viewers were dispelled when Sophronia gasped a sob. *I still pressed her to my breast and continued to walk the floor. She sobbed again, then looked up into my face, and commenced breathing quite freely. My soul was satisfied, but my strength was gone. I laid my daughter on the bed, and sunk by her side, completely overpowered by the intensity of my feelings.*

God blessed my daughter to continue healing. However, a quick and dramatic recovery was not possible for my son, Joseph Jr., then seven years of age. When he fell ill with the fever, it at first seemed to have but a mild effect, especially compared to my other children's experiences. He was ill with the disease for about two weeks and then recovered. The problems that were of concern to us grew from the unexpected aftereffect of the illness.

We found out about the trouble while we sat around the table during dinner. Suddenly Joseph Jr. complained about a pain in his shoulder. This pain grew worse until he reached the point *he appeared to be in such agony, that we feared the consequences would prove to be something very serious.* Refusing to take any chances at what might be ailing him, we sent for Dr. Parker. Not long after the doctor arrived, he went through a complete examination and ascertained that Joseph had sprained his shoulder.

"I did not," Joseph said.

"You must have landed on it hard, falling out of a tree or something," Dr. Parker answered.

"I did no such thing. I did not land on my shoulder while doing anything."

"You must have," the doctor said and listened to Joseph no longer. He was satisfied he had found the answer.

An agonizing wave of pain attacked Joseph and we then ignored all thoughts of what the doctor said. The doctor jumped into action, treating the sprain by rubbing bone liniment into the hurting shoulder. He also used applications of a hot shovel. The doctor declared, "Joseph will soon be back to normal." And he left.

When two weeks of extreme suffering had passed, Dr. Parker was called in again to see what could be done. By this point, I was tense about my boy and the incredible pain God was calling on him to bear. My heart yearned to stop the suffering for little Joseph. Dr. Parker made further investigations. This time he found *a large fever sore had gathered between his breast and shoulder. He immediately lanced* the large abscess, *upon which it discharged fully a quart of matter.* The sore began to heal and I breathed easier, thinking our troubles were about over.

When the abscess drained and we all were in awe at the infection leaving his shoulder, Joseph complained that a pain *shot like lightening (using his own terms) down his side into the marrow of the bone of his leg.* For two weeks my son suffered as his leg swelled. The infection had traveled from his armpit into the marrow of his leg.

My poor poor boy, at this, was almost in despair, and he, cried out "Oh, father! The pain is so severe, how can I bear it!" I sought for what could be done to help relieve the pain and found that if I carried my son in my arms, he did not suffer as intensly. Because this was the case, I carried him as much as I could. His size and weight at seven was considerable for me. This lifting, and my worry over all my children as we warred against this deadly foe, must have been harder on me than I realized, for I fell ill. To see one's children suffering incredibly and not be able to muster the strength to aid them was the hardest cross to bear.

Hyrum, yearning for Joseph to experience any relief from the agony, and to aid me in my situation, sat by Joseph's low bed almost all day and night, bracing Joseph's hurting leg in his hands to help lessen his younger brother's pain. The tenderness between these two boys, and what Hyrum was so willing to suffer for Joseph's benefit, touched me deeply.

The agony Joseph suffered stretched on for three weeks without relenting. At this point my husband decided something more drastic needed to be done. Hyrum had grown weary and Joseph had begun to lose his determination to fight. My husband fetched a surgeon, this time hoping that a proper draining of the leg would heal his son's body.

We had heard of a surgeon, a Dr. Nathan Smith, who held a degree from Dartmouth College at nearby Hanover. After examining Joseph Jr.'s condition, the surgeon agreed with our recommendation that the opening of the leg to release the infection was the best course of action. My son was so young and the treatment so aggressive, but I could not stand him suffering any longer. When the surgeon began the procedure, Joseph bore the surgery with hardly a movement or a whimper. The cut was eight inches, from his knee to his ankle. A great amount of fluid drained from his leg, and with it went the pain until the leg began to heal. But to my horror, the leg swelled up again and Joseph's suffering was the same as before. My husband and I discussed the matter at length, our trust in the doctor's ability waning.

Joseph felt that if a group of surgeons were called together and they reached a consensus on what to do, our son would then be under the best care. A council of surgeons, seven all together, came from Dartmouth Medical College.

The house grew solemn as they gathered into the small room where my boy lay in such agony. As the leaders in the medical field consulted among themselves, my heart pounded. I stood by my husband, pressing his hand until my own fingers ached. The head surgeon turned to us and said, "Mr. and Mrs. Smith, we have gone over this grave condition extensively and have reached the conclusion that if we are going to save this boy's life, it is necessary to amputate his leg. *We have cut it open to the bone, and find it so affected that we consider his leg incurable, and that amputation is absolutely necessary in order to save his life.*"

"No," I cried from a pain deep within me. "No."

"Mrs. Smith, we understand your feelings regarding this measure, but the infection will soon consume his body and at that point his life will be taken."

"There has to be another way," I said.

"I am afraid, Mrs. Smith, that—" the head surgeon began.

"Can you not make another trial? Can you not, by cutting around the bone, take out the diseased part, and perhaps that which is sound will heal over, and by this means you save his leg? You will not, you must not, take off his leg, until you try once more. I will not consent to let you enter his room until you make me this promise."

"That would be a radical procedure—"

"But it could work," I said, feeling a deep conviction that my son's leg needed to be saved.

"There is a possibility," said another of the surgeons.

Thus the conversation went back and forth in a similar manner until at last the surgeons consented to try my idea, and we entered Joseph's room.

Dr. Smith approached my son. *"My poor boy, we have come again."*

My son bravely acknowledged this statement and looked the doctor straight in the eyes before asking, "Have you come to take my leg?"

"Not this time," the doctor answered. "And that you can thank your mother for. She has convinced us to try taking out the bad part of the bone and see if that rids you of your awful ordeal. It will be a severe operation, but you seem to have the substance that will be necessary to endure such a task."

Three doctors and my husband went to work over whether Joseph Jr. was to be tied down and whether he would drink liquor to aid him through the pain. Both things my boy refused to do, and it became clear that it would be useless to argue with him.

Shaken and pale as he was, Joseph looked up and said, *"Mother, I want you to leave the room, for I know you cannot bear to see me suffer so;*

Father can stand it, but you have carried me so much, and watched over me so long, you are almost worn out." Then looking up into my face, his eyes swimming in tears, he continued, *"Now, Mother, promise me that you will not stay, will you? The Lord will help me, and I will get through with it."*

I was torn by my desire to be at my son's side, yet I wanted to honor his request. I found clean sheets and put them under his leg before I left the room.

My heart, mind, and soul begged to stand next to him and hold his hand and know what was happening. That not being possible, I walked outside as he requested, my younger children following after me. I stumbled over the uneven fields, praying and hoping that the beauty of nature would take my mind away from the scene inside our home. The calm that nature offered was disturbed when a horrendous scream sounded from the cabin.

I could stay away no longer. I rushed from the field toward the house and into his room, gasping. Sprawled on the bed lay my seven-year-old son, his face pallid white, perspiration drenching him. Pure agony bent his body into contorted shapes as pain racked his being. Not even a gasp could escape from my constricted throat as I beheld the scene. The surgeon had started the operation by boring into the infected bone of his leg, then breaking the other side of his bone until they could break off big chunks with pincers.

"Joseph, can't you do something for the pain?" I begged my husband.

"Mother . . . leave," Joseph Jr. said, struggling through a wave of pain. *"Go back, go back; I do not want you to come in—I will try to tough it out, if you will go away."*

A doctor ushered me from the room and there I stayed until I heard another horrible scream. I raced back to see what could be done to stop Joseph's pain. Blood oozed and dripped everywhere; the bed and Joseph's leg were a red mess. His face was wet with sweat, and if it were not for the agony, the stark paleness would have made me think he was dead. I caught my husband's eyes for a brief moment. I saw he, too, was tormented.

The surgeon, growing impatient with my interruptions, rushed me from the room. Shamed, I forced myself onto the doorstep to be greeted by Alvin. He gave me a cup of water, motioned me to sit, then put his hand on my slumped shoulder. I poured out my soul in prayer. Another scream came and Alvin held me back. Some of my children had gathered around, watching me with tears in their eyes. I refrained from any more emotion for my children's sakes.

The wait was long before the signal was given and I was permitted to enter my boy's room. Joseph lay on the bed, weak, but resting. The strength was drained out of him. The doctor had cleaned the blood and instruments that had caused me such a fright. The room showed no evidence of the drastic measures that had taken place only minutes before.

I rushed to Joseph and kissed his clammy, pale skin, silently offering multiple prayers of thanks that his life was spared. "Please, Lord," I prayed, "if I could ask one more favor, that this would be the last surgery my boy would have to endure for his leg."

The whole family remained nervous the next couple of weeks as we waited to see if the surgery was a success. The recovery was a slow, painstaking ordeal, but from that time on Joseph's leg improved. He lost a lot of weight because he was confined in the bed, but that made moving him much easier.

The doctors from New York had been expensive, but they were the most skilled and they did save young Joseph's life. His recovery marked a time of renewed good fortune for our family, which continued for the next three years.

Chapter 6

$\mathcal{I}$n the spring of 1816, my husband planted his crops with high hopes of harvesting enough food to sell to pay off the mounting medical bills. After he finished with his work and waited for the crops to grow, a frost crawled across Norwich, Vermont, killing the new plants. Then came ice and with it snow. This continued throughout the early growing season. Our sense of desperation increased along with it.

By the time summer arrived, yet another frost set in, killing our plants, making it impossible to yield the necessary crop. My husband surrendered. He gave up all hope of carving out an existence in this land so he set out to find a new place that might offer a better living. On his journeys he found himself drawn to the southern part of New York State, the Genesee region. The city he decided on was Palmyra, in Wayne County, with three thousand inhabitants. The place was booming! The city was doing so well that it had attracted people of many professions. Palmyra boasted four taverns, a drugstore, distillery, harness shop, tannery and a bookstore.

Each person in the family pitched in and saved enough money to make the move. I was able to bring a lot of money in by painting oil tablecloths and selling them. This was a hobby I much enjoyed, and I felt blessed that I could earn money for doing something that encouraged my creativity. Other members in the family also contributed. Some of them sold refreshments from a small shop and peddled their wares by cart when crowds gathered for celebrations at revivals. Our sons were helpful by working for farmers who needed extra hands for harvesting, digging wells, and landscaping. We made and sold potash and pearl ash from burnt trees. We also cut cordwood, sold the maple sugar we collected, and grew corn. We sold items such as brooms, baskets, cakes, maple sugar, and molasses. Our boys also fished, trapped, and hunted, providing us with much of the food we lived on.

When enough money was earned, Joseph sent for us. He did not intend for us to move alone. In the midst of making plans, we talked with a Mr. Howard who was also traveling to Palmyra. He offered to accompany my children and me to see that we arrived safely. This eased my husband's worry.

Another concern that had to be resolved before we could leave was to settle the debts we owed. My husband had an uneasy feeling that if he left without our debts being paid, the creditors would come after us and this could put us in a vulnerable position. I proposed we call a meeting with all the creditors and debtors and during that meeting reach resolutions. My husband agreed; he reached a settlement with all concerned.

With our financial situation addressed, my husband went on ahead to Palmyra, trusting that, between my mother and me, we could handle the move. My mother, as always, was a great blessing in helping me prepare for the journey. She worked along with my children packing and obtaining the provisions we would need. She

planned on traveling part of the way with us, leaving when we reached the home of my brother, Daniel Mack, in Royalton.

After much work, we were ready to set out on the trip. As previously arranged, we waited for word to come that our team was en route. Finally word was sent. We gathered the last of our things, and I traveled to all my neighbors' houses saying goodbye to the good people who had touched our lives.

At last I said farewell to my log home. We were moving again because of mounting medical bills from Joseph Jr.'s leg operation, failed crops, and because we had been taken advantage of in business deals. Still, despite these hardships and others, I felt a sadness at leaving.

We had traveled but a short distance from our log home when a group of men on horseback stopped us. "Mrs. Smith," one of the leading men said, "you were not planning on leaving this area without paying off your debts, were you?"

"What are you talking about?" I asked, looking into their smirking faces. "We've made good on all our debts."

"That is not the truth," the grinning man said.

He had written up a false claim in the books. We had, in front of witnesses, made good on all the debts that he claimed, yet he said that was not the truth. I longed for my husband to be there by my side as I was bone tired and unsure how to proceed. Joseph would have known how to deal with these thieves. Whereas I was a woman with eight children ranging in age from four to seventeen. I asked for time to deal with a situation of which I was clearly unaware. They laughed. "Mrs. Smith, are you trying to slip out of town without making good on your debts?" I retired home and underwent considerable efforts to raise the money they were insisting on, one hundred and fifty dollars in total.

Quite a few people were unhappy with what they saw happening to us. Two of the most upset were *a gentleman by the name of Flagg, a wealthy settler, living in the town of Hanover, also a Mr. Howard, who resided in Norwich.*

They urged me to give them time to bring witnesses together and take this situation to court where it could be resolved honestly. I thought this over but concluded that I should do no such thing.

I was tired and I missed my husband, but I could not give in. The other more weighty matter to consider was the daily money being charged for the team. I could not afford, in my present situation, to fight these dishonest men. Another consideration was that I had no guarantee I would get the money; the odds were heavy that I would lose the money they claimed I owed and also the money I spent daily for the team. If failure was the outcome, I would not have enough funds to make the move. That was too much of a risk.

Mr. Flagg and Mr. Howard proposed raising money by subscription, saying, *"We know the people feel as we do concerning this matter, and if you will receive it, we will make you a handsome present."*

I would not hear of such a thing. The fact that my husband was away and thieves had hatched up a scheme to rid me of my funds did not mean I would become a beggar to my neighbors and friends. I paid the fabricated bill and left on the journey with eight children and my mother by my side. I had less than eighty dollars to see us to Palmyra. When asked by one of my children how we were going to do it, I gathered my will and said, "The Lord will see us through."

I wish I could say that was the end of my troubles, but another hardship befell us in the form of an accident. The wagon was traversing up a slope when the front wheel hit a rock at the wrong angle, overturning the wagon and its precious cargo. The accident caused bruises, bumps, and sprains, although the worst injury was sustained by Mother. Seeing my mother, the woman who had loved me, supported me, cried with me, and shared in our family's happiness, injured and bleeding, sprawled out on the ground, brought feelings I cannot easily describe. I sensed this injury would prove fatal.

Eventually we arrived in Royalton, stopping at my brother Daniel Mack's home. I was to leave Mother at the tavern of Willard Pierce. There she and I made quite a scene at our departure from each other. *It was truly a severe one—one to which I shall ever look back with peculiar feelings. Here I was to take leave of my affectionate mother. The parting hour came; my mother wept over me, long and bitterly. She told me that it was not probable she should ever behold my face again; "But, my dear child," she said, "I have lived long—my days are nearly numbered—I must soon exchange the things of this world for those which pertain to another state of existence, where I hope to enjoy the society of the blessed; and now as my last admonition, I beseech you to continue faithful in the service of God to the end of your days, that I may have the pleasure of embracing you in another and fairer world above."*

From Royalton, we progressed toward Palmyra, which lay three hundred miles to the west. This was a considerable distance to travel at any time, but with the driver we had, Caleb Howard, the miles sprawled on endlessly. Caleb was a heartless, crude man who tried my ability to find virtue in every soul. I had to call on my Maker and beg for powers of patience and restraint in dealing with him. I found no emotion harder to control than the anguish and anger of a mother seeing one of her young ones being wronged. To my great horror, it was my little Joseph that Caleb took a great disliking to.

Two years had passed since Joseph Jr.'s operation. Only recently had he been able to discard his crutches. Seeing my son hobble, Caleb made jeering comments around the campfire when we halted for a rest. He laughed and said, "Joe, that is just a show for sympathy. It's not going to work."

This torment continued endlessly until one day, jeering and laughing wasn't enough for Caleb. He climbed up the side of the wagon, looked Joseph in the face and said, "Out."

"What?" I asked.

"Your boy needs to get out now," he said. "I can't drive this wagon any farther with him in it. He can walk. I have watched him. There is no reason for him to get special treatment."

"He's injured from a surgery," Alvin said.

"He's barely gotten off his crutches," Hyrum pleaded. "There's no reason why he cannot ride."

"I will not have my boy walk," I interrupted. "We paid you to do this."

His hard eyes looked at mine before he said, "Well, I have your money so we'll do it my way."

There was nothing I could say to that.

The reason Caleb would not let Joseph ride became apparent when he escorted two young girls into the wagon to sit beside him. Along the way we had fallen in line with a family named Gates who traveled in the same direction. The Gates' daughters were naïve and good-looking and had taken a liking to Caleb, although I could not understand why.

The girls laughed and squealed with Caleb, as my boy suffered pain from his wounded leg as we headed toward Palmyra. Caleb at times would have Joseph walk for miles until my poor boy was in so much hurt I wondered whether he could go on.

This treatment was almost more than I could bear and was certainly more than Alvin and Hyrum could stand. One day, my boys headed toward Caleb to make things right, but he drew a whip and knocked both my sons down with it. The snapping sound of leather against their skin caused me to shudder.

The trip continued as we suffered under the abusive hand of our team driver. He spent our money on drinking and gambling at night. His language, mannerisms, and behavior were all of great offense, but none of that topped what he did when we were twenty miles from Utica, about one hundred miles from our final destination.

We had camped and I awoke earlier than normal to a noise. It was before dawn and I could barely make out shadows. I rose, walked toward the sound and saw Caleb throw the last of our belongings out of the wagon. Seeing me, he hurried to the front of the wagon, snapped the reins and headed off in a heated rush.

It took a couple of hours to find Mr. Caleb Howard, but men like him sink into their weakness and filthiness. He was where I thought he would be, indulging himself in a bar, which was filled with many men and women who were also traveling. I walked into that bar without flinching. "Mr. Howard," I said in a voice filled with the anger I felt toward him, his actions, and his character, being that of an *unprincipled and unfeeling wretch*. "I would like to know the meaning of your throwing out all my belongings from my wagon and taking off like you did, leaving myself and my eight children stranded."

His eyes grew wide as he glanced around the bar that had grown thick with quiet. "Mrs. Smith, what has happened sorrows me greatly, but you have run out of money and I can go no farther without more money."

There was some nodding of understanding. I turned toward those people present and spoke loudly and clearly so all could hear. *"Gentlemen and ladies, please give your attention for a moment. Now, as sure as there is a God in heaven, that team, as well as the goods, belong to my husband, and this man intends to take them from me, or at least the team, leaving me with eight children, without the means of proceeding on my journey."* Then turning to Mr. Howard, I said, *"Sir, I now forbid you touching the team, or driving it one step further. You can go about your own business; I have no use for you. I shall take charge of the team myself, and hereafter attend to my own affairs."*

To this, Mr. Howard hurried out of the bar and attempted to get on the wagon. I grabbed the reins from his hands as my children mounted the wagon. Somebody in the crowd took Mr. Howard off the seat. I drove the team in the midst of a loud, enthusiastic, cheering crowd. My children cheered too. This excitement boosted us on our journey. From then on, we paid innkeepers with clothing and yards of cloth in exchange for food and a place to sleep. We arrived in Palmyra with less than a few cents, but we were safe and back together as a family.

Chapter 7

The spring in Palmyra gave me glimpses of what lay in store for us if we lived worthy to earn the glory of the eternities. The magnificence of the array and depth of colors bursting forth contrasting with the drab of winter was dramatic. One early morning I was appreciating and enjoying the treasures God gives us in nature while I hung the wash. I glanced up once more to take in the mountains, clouds, and sky when Joseph, our fourth son, walked out of the woods. This wasn't unusual as many of us in the family retreated to the woods for quiet contemplations with God. But this time, his walk wasn't the same easy pace of his signature gait. Instead his posture slumped and it seemed as if he was dragging himself home. Curious, yet not overly concerned with this oddity, I watched him.

He made his way to his father out in the field. I took one more appreciative glance at the natural beauty around me and relished the knowledge that I had been so blessed. I returned to the house to continue my chores. When the door opened, I looked up to see my son. His face was pale and his body slumped weakly, yet he glowed, his eyes reflecting a brightness that seemed to spring from deep within him. He struggled to the fireplace and leaned against it. I inquired what was bothering him.

"Never mind," he said, "I am well enough off."[11] After what seemed to be a long while he added, "I have learned for myself that Presbyterianism is not true."

Joseph Jr. would later write: "It seems thus though the adversary was aware, at a very early period of my life, that I was destined to prove a disturber and an annoyer of his kingdom; else why should the powers of darkness combine against me? Why the opposition and persecution that arose against me, almost in my infancy?"[12]

Our son Joseph, at the age of fourteen, had asked many of the same questions that our family had been asking for generations. Which church is true? Why do the churches not follow the patterns set out in the Bible? How are we to know where God wants us to demonstrate our love and faith?

Little did I know that the much sought after answers had been revealed moments before. Joseph spoke, his voice full of energy, about retreating to the trees to pray as I had supposed. He had a vision where God the Father and His Son came down from Their thrones and visited him to tell him none of the churches were correct. These heavenly Beings instructed that further information on establishing the true church would come to him.

When I heard this experience from my son's trembling lips, knowing he wasn't one for wild imaginations, and also knowing him to be true of character, I searched his face, his eyes, and studied his countenance. There was no doubt that this incredible tale was the truth. I had received answers many times, not quite so dramatic, and Joseph Sr. had dreams that forewarned us of such an event. God had clearly prepared us for this glorious day. I rested my hand on the hearth for support. I, too, had become afflicted with weakness. The gracious Lord up above loved my boy, myself, the whole earth enough to bring this most joyful news to us. My boy was the instrument through whom the Lord had chosen to bring His message. It was an honor. We now knew without doubt that God lived and He was personally involved in our lives and He was going to see that the truth was brought back to the earth! This joy carried me throughout the rest of my life. It has lightened my burdens and allowed me to find much happiness in the midst of hardship. I have spread this joyful news to all I can find who will listen.

Our whole family experienced much happiness over receiving such an awing answer. I tell the truth of these happenings. Some, maybe more, won't believe this story. Some say my boy made it up for attention or power. I testify this was not the case. My son suffered most horribly for this experience, but nevertheless, he held firm to his testimony. I also will die with the testimony of the truthfulness of this account on my lips.

Later, Joseph Jr. saw an angel, Moroni, who repeatedly visited him. This angel instructed Joseph to live God's laws. He informed Joseph that if he achieved the right level of knowledge and showed his ability to follow God more than man, he would receive golden plates that contained the history of the native peoples of this continent. We did not know what those plates disclosed, but we did know it would be important for our salvation. Our family was anxious for Joseph to fulfill what was required of him, so we could obtain the plates and learn more of God's laws and ways.

Chapter 8

One of the saddest events the Lord saw fit to have me go through happened five years after we moved to Palmyra. The situation started out on the bright side but it will always cause tears to rise to my eyes. In 1823, Alvin, my oldest son, decided to build a home for my husband and me. In his tender heart, he wanted to make sure Joseph and I lived out our remaining years in comfort.

Alvin's aspirations were admirable. At the age of twenty-three, he started work on a wood-frame house. He became the chief manager of the project. He said, *"I am going to have a nice, pleasant room for father and mother to sit in, and everything arranged for their comfort, and they shall not work any more as they have done."*

Joseph and I were very much touched by his efforts and his desires for us. If we hadn't run into bad business arrangements in our earlier years, we wouldn't have been without a home, but since that did happen, our dear boy wished us to have as much physical happiness as he could provide.

The house was turning out beautifully. Alvin was gifted in craftsmanship. The anticipation of moving into our new home, built by our boy, and spending our remaining days there, was great. By November 15, 1824, a good portion of the house had been built.

Alvin stumbled home that day in an immense amount of pain. "Father, please go for a physician," he said within moments after arriving home and staggering to bed.

Joseph, seeing that our son suffered so, immediately left to seek relief for Alvin from what we were to later learn was bilious colic. Joseph, unable to find our family's physician, employed a nearby doctor by the name of Greenwood. The doctor immediately came to Alvin's side and, after examination, determined that calomel, a heavy white compound of chloride and mercury that was used as a purgative, would aid Alvin back to health.

Alvin disagreed with Dr. Greenwood. "That is not what I need," he said. "I will not take it."

The doctor spoke to him at length as to why this medicine was needed and what it would do to help him recover. At last, Alvin agreed to take the medication.

We watched Alvin with hopeful eyes to make certain the symptoms of his illness faded as the doctor had promised. Instead, my dear boy grew worse. He complained that the medicine Dr. Greenwood gave him had not done what the doctor claimed, but instead had lodged at the bottom of his stomach and was causing him discomfort. He also predicted the medicine would kill him.

Oh, to hear a son speak thus and to know that he spoke with absolute conviction was enough to put me in the grave. I sought out as many physicians as I could find to help. I often found myself on my knees, pleading with the Lord. At this point in my spiritual development, I knew that I must trust God with the verdict, but I also knew He heard and often answered prayers. In the midst of one of my pleadings, I had an overwhelming sense that things would be all right. I put my trust in that.

We called other physicians in, hoping they could prescribe something to rid Alvin of the colic and the effects of the medicine Dr. Greenwood had given him. The doctors tried many things, but nothing brought relief. Continuously our son talked about feeling the chunk of medicine eating at his stomach.

After the last physician left, Alvin came to the conclusion that he would pass away. With that resolve, he turned to his brother and said, *"Hyrum, I must die. Now I want to say a few things, which I wish to have you remember. I have done all I could to make our parents comfortable. I want you to go on and finish the house and take care of them in their old age, and do not any more let them work hard, as they are now in old age."*

I could not keep the tears from my eyes. Like Christ, whose thoughts turned to his mother and the care she would receive when He was gone, my Alvin thought about me and his father as he lay dying.

Alvin also had other family members on his mind in his last hours. After conversing with Hyrum, he asked to say some things to Sophronia. He spoke thus: *"Sophronia, you must be a good girl, and do all you can for father and mother—never forsake them; they have worked hard, and they are now getting old. Be kind to them, and remember what they have done for us."*

There was no more talk of death until the next night. It was then he called the children into the house and his bedside. He spoke to them in much the same way he had spoken to Sophronia and Hyrum. But he counseled with Joseph Jr. in a much different manner. He said, *"I am now going to die, the distress which I suffer, and the feelings that I have, tell me my time is very short. I want you to be a good boy, and do everything that lies in your power to obtain the Record. Be faithful in receiving instruction, and in keeping every commandment that is given you. Your brother Alvin must leave you; but remember the example which he has set for you; and set the same example for the children that are younger than yourself, and always be kind to father and mother."*

The "Record" that Alvin referred to would later be called the Book of Mormon. He had been very passionate about seeing this come to pass. As I listened to him counsel his younger brother on how to be successful in accomplishing God's commandment, my heart grew heavy with the realization that Alvin would not live to see the work fulfilled.

After Alvin counseled Joseph thus, he turned and asked for little Lucy, our youngest daughter. Alvin and little Lucy always had a special bond. Often I would find them together, enjoying each other's company. Little Lucy had taken a liking to Alvin's lap, and he had taken to stroking her hair and gently teasing her. Seeing the brother and sister together touched many a cold heart.

As requested, I fetched little Lucy, who was still very young. I awoke her from her sleep. "Alvin wants to see you."

She wiped her eyes. *"Amby, Amby." We took her to him, and when she got within reach of him, she sprang from my arms and caught him around the neck, and cried out, "Oh! Amby,"* and kissed him some more.

"Lucy," he said, *"you must be the best girl in the world, and take care of mother; you can't have your Amby any more. Amby is going away; he must leave little Lucy." He then kissed her, and said, "Take her away, I think my breath offends her." We took hold of her to take her away; but she clinched him with such a strong grasp, that it was with difficulty we succeeded in disengaging her hands.*

When we separated brother and sister, Alvin said, *"Farewell family."* His spirit then ascended to heaven. Little Lucy burst into gasping cries, asking her brother to come back to her. She continued to lunge for him until I relented and let her throw her arms around him once more. She hugged him, covered him with kisses, and cried uncontrollably.

The grief gripped her so tightly that I took her outside in hopes to settle her troubled soul. This was to no avail. I wondered if she represented all our feelings at losing our dear Alvin, and at the same time our longing to pull him close to us, hugging and kissing him in an effort to hold onto that great soul whose presence we had been blessed with for over twenty-three years.

Little Lucy was not the only person to grieve over Alvin's death. In fact, the grief was widespread, for many in our neighborhood were much saddened upon hearing he had gone from us. Many people felt compelled to attend his funeral, and much sympathy was directed toward us.

Our sadness was increased when, upon the request of the chief physician, Alvin was cut open to determine the cause of death. The doctors found the calomel medicine lodged in his upper bowels, almost in the same state as when swallowed. The physician also found gangrene surrounding the lodged mass.

With the evidence that Alvin had been right, the sadness of his untimely death pressed on me. It seemed so useless to lose my dear boy at the hands of an incompetent professional. If only we had hearkened to Alvin's impressions, he would still be with us. These thoughts, along with many others, ran through my mind many times until at last I had to halt any further "if onlys." Instead I deemed that

Alvin's passing was God's will and I thought about how he was now with my sisters and the other children I had lost. Despite the fact that I came to accept God's will, I found it almost impossible to find comfort.

I did, however, attach myself to the loving gesture Alvin had been engaged in right before his passing, that being the building of our home. With mixed feelings I wandered through the rooms and caressed the wood of the frame. I was much moved to have the opportunity to be the mother of such a soul as his, and yet, as I touched the wood and the nails that he had held and crafted, the bitter pain of my loss was always present.

Time passed, until I believed that Alvin was paving the way in heaven before me and perhaps helping with Joseph getting the plates. I was thinking about that and my good fortune at being his mother, as I gazed out my window. It was then I saw several men heading toward our home. One of the gentlemen that had come to pay a visit was now the principal carpenter of the home, Mr. Stoddard. I invited them into our house and asked them to be seated, although curious at the unfriendly manner in which they addressed me. I sorely wished my husband had been present, but he was away from home. My curiosity was soon to be satisfied. "When did you make your last payment on your home?" one man blurted out.

"I, um—" I started to answer, only to be interrupted.

"Do you wish to sell?"

"Sell the house!" I replied, "No, sir, we have no occasion for that, we have made every necessary arrangement to get the deed, and also have an understanding with the agent. So you see we are quite secure, in regard to this matter."

Although I said I was secure in the matter, I had seen too many dishonest dealings take place and I had no faith that these men had any desire but to do me wrong. The fact that they would not listen to my response and immediately sought Hyrum only raised my suspicions.

The men received no further information upon questioning my son, who had answered in a similar fashion as myself. On the other hand, they gave us additional information.

"Hyrum, we advise you to do no more work on the farm, for it is not yours any longer."

"What?" he asked, searching each of their faces for the meaning of such a statement.

With a smile Mr. Stoddard said, *"We have bought the place, and paid for it, and we now forbid your touching anything on the farm; and we also warn you to leave forthwith, and give possession to the lawful owners."*

All the breath in my lungs squeezed out with his last declaration. Our house, our farm, the parting gift and our connection to Alvin, gone. This could not be. I would not accept what these men said, and neither, I supposed, would Hyrum. I looked at the men to determine if they spoke the truth or if they were meaning only to frighten us. From the dark satisfied expression they gave, I knew they had done what they said.

My legs gave out from under me and I slumped to the floor in shock. After I revived, I talked at length with these men who were determined to steal our home from us. No matter how I pleaded or tried to convince these men to have mercy or that I would be willing to pay them what they asked, they would not listen.

After the men left, I asked Hyrum, "What is to be done?"

"We need to consult with Dr. Robinson about what has befallen us."

Dr. Robinson was an old family friend who had influence in this part of the country. "We should see," I said, responding to Hyrum's idea, "if he would write a letter about the character of our family and what hard-working people we are, and that we always pay our responsibilities."

Hyrum hurried away to ask if Dr. Robinson was willing to do this for us. Not only did he write the letter, but he wrote at length of his confidence and impression of our family at large. He then traveled through town for about an hour and had sixty subscribers sign his composition. When he had completed this task, he asked Hyrum if he would be so kind as to deliver the papers to the land agent who lived in Canandaigua.

Hyrum was more than willing to engage in any attempt to save our home. With much anxiousness, he rushed to the agent.

Our son's crestfallen face told all upon his return, although I listened to see how the events unfolded. He had hurried to the land agent, hoping that delivering the papers in a timely manner would reverse or halt the foreclosure on our home. This wasn't to be the case.

When the land agent examined the paper and the signatures of all the people who had vouched for us, he most clearly saw there was ill intent toward us. He proceeded regretfully to explain why he had done what he did. "The men came to me most worried. Their concern was to learn if I knew what was happening to my property. I told them I did not. 'Well,' they said, 'Mr. Smith and his son ran away, leaving the house in the hands of Hyrum and Mrs. Smith.'"

It was true. My husband had left to secure money for the last payments needed on the house before we could obtain the deed. My son, Joseph, was engaged in a very different type of pursuit. His heart had been taken by a beautiful young girl named Emma. He left in hopes of making her his wife, which pleased me. Emma was the daughter of Isaac Hale who had boarded Joseph when he worked for Mr. Stoal, digging up silver.

The men said that while the father and son were gone, Hyrum had become out of control with extreme destructive behavior, ruining the property in mischievous fits. He was now cutting down the sugar orchard, had hauled off the rails, was burning them, and other similar deeds.

"These are all lies," Hyrum had said.

At this point, the owner shook his head, the wrinkles on his face and brow deepening. "I believed this tale. And you must trust me, I feared I was going to lose my investment if you continued with the reported destruction. When they offered to buy the house and land from me at a reasonable price, I felt fortunate to not lose my money and quickly sold your house to them."

Upon hearing the land agent's response, I could understand why he did what he had done and I did not hold ill feelings toward him. The seller immediately contacted the people who had purchased our home and tried to resolve the problem. Despite these efforts, the men wanted our home and they refused any compromise. Instead they repeated over and over, *"We've got the land, sir, and we've got the deed, so just let Smith help himself. Oh, no matter about Smith, he has gold plates, gold Bibles, he is rich—he don't want anything."*

These jeering words had an ironic effect on me and my heart. I could recognize them for what they were. My family and I were being persecuted for the truth, for following God. If God came down and was directing my family to get the gold plates which would be of great benefit to the world, surely we were going to undergo many of the same challenges and hardships that others who had followed Christ were called upon to experience.

Thus it became apparent that we were losing the roof over our heads. *The anxiety of mind that I suffered . . . can more easily be imagined than described. I now looked upon the proceeds of our industry, which smiled around us on every hand, with a kind of yearning attachment that I never before had experienced; and our early losses I did not feel so keenly, for I then realized that we were young, and by making some exertions we might improve our circumstances.* This time, though, the misery of it was more terrible, not only because of my age and the age of my husband, but because of the memory that had been built into the very structure of the frame of the home. The loss of Alvin and his dream for us rested heavily upon me.

Chapter 9

The mobs and persecution were a constant in my life because of Joseph Jr. and the gold plates, and the religion God restored through him. I do not want to dwell too much on what those savages did to me, my sons, my daughters, my husband, and many of the good Saints who believed in Joseph and the gospel. However, I will go into detail about one of the worst situations I was personally faced with at the age of 55.

It was spring of 1831. Men of darkness forced the members of the Church to flee from their homes for their very lives. Close to one hundred members of the Church in New York had made their way to Kirtland, Ohio. My husband and my sons, Samuel and Hyrum, left before me, anxious to join Joseph Jr. and give him much-needed help with the work there.

This left me in charge of taking eighty souls to Kirtland. We departed in early May and rented a flatboat, which we boarded on a canal from the dock on the Seneca River. This passage followed the Cayuga and Erie Canal to Buffalo.

The first obstacle we encountered was a great drop in temperature, which caused heavy ice to form on Lake Erie. The ice became so thick it blocked our passage. No boat was able to pass.

In my group there were about thirty children, which increased the confusion. They had grown tired and restless as we stood in the cold, waiting for the ice to break. Many of the women had resorted to crying and whining, believing all was lost.

I walked to the boat's rail and leaned over it to gasp some air. I felt my age. I was disgusted with the women's behavior and lack of faith. As I pondered the situation, I felt a great pressure to hold everyone up. Regaining my resolve, I told the sisters to *lift their hearts in prayer to God.* At last the Saints joined together in uniting their faith and God heard our prayers. Suddenly a loud crack sounded from the ice. The ice drifted apart enough for our boat to pass through. Once our boat had sailed through the opening in the ice, it closed up again and allowed no other boat passage. Great appreciation swept through our company, although the water was choppy, which produced a sickness among most in the company. To aid ourselves against the wind and the movement, we huddled together on the deck for protection. This helped somewhat against the sinking temperature.

We traveled in this manner until at last the boat rocked over the final few waves and landed at Fairport, not far from Cleveland. We continued the remainder of the journey by land, fatigued and cold, but grateful for the ground beneath our feet.

When we arrived in Kirtland, we made an extremely sorry sight. We were disorganized despite my efforts to lead, and all in my company were tired, hungry, and homeless. There was little food or money available and no opportunity to secure any. This left us in the most unfortunate condition of relying on the hospitality of local members until we were able to reestablish ourselves on farms, or in business or trade.

May the Lord have mercy on the dear Saints who so willingly took us in when their conditions weren't much better than our own. I truly believe the kindness and goodness they showed us will return to them greatly multiplied.

I will speak only briefly about Kirtland. Hoping to avoid persecution, Joseph and Emma moved there where part of the Church was growing. While in Kirtland, many men were called to serve missions. Consequently, the women spent countless long hours preparing adequate clothing for the men. This was an arduous task as they had to make the cloth from raw material. My favorite part was stitching the different pieces of fabric together.

One of the hardest workers was my dear daughter-in-law, Emma. Her *health at this time was quite delicate, yet she did not favor herself on this account, but whatever her hands found to do, she did with her might, until she went so far beyond her strength that she brought upon herself a heavy fit of sickness, which lasted four weeks. And, although her strength was exhausted, still her spirits were the same, which, in fact, was always the case with her, even under the most trying circumstances.* I will always have a deep love and respect for this noble woman.

She suffered under the trials the Lord deemed fit to place on her. She longed for children, she longed for her husband to be by her side, she prayed for safety and an end to the stress and worry that seemed to contantly torment her. She hid from others the strain she was under. She was a delightful conversationalist and knew how to hide from watchful eyes the fear she felt. When my son Joseph was tarred and feathered, nightmares began to afflict her as she worried about more ill treatment to her husband and as she grieved over the loss of yet another baby. I tried my best to be a comfort to her.

At Kirtland, in 1835, I actively engaged in preaching God's word to all with whom I came in contact. I gave out copies of the Book of Mormon and many people were overcome with its truthfulness and joined the Church. I devoted any free time I had to studying the Bible, the Book of Mormon, and the Doctrine and Covenants.

I also participated in helping build the temple. This was an exciting work. The Lord was reestablishing his holy dwelling as in the times of old. Joseph Jr. had been shown a glorious vision of what the temple was to be like, which we thought on many times when criticism was muttered that a less elaborate building would serve the purpose.

When Joseph Jr. told us that this work was to be done many Saints had already been driven out of Kirtland. There was much fear of what the mob would do next. The idea of not only trying to protect ourselves and families from the mob, but also of building a temple of the proportions Joseph described was overwhelming, but the work did not *stop until it was accomplished*. All the remaining Saints *endured great fatigue and privation, in consequence of the opposition they met with from their enemies, and which was so great, that they were compelled to keep a guard around the walls much of the time.*

While the men engaged in the actual building of the temple, I gathered the ladies around me and those who boarded with me to *devote their time to making and mending clothes for the men.* As we engaged in this task, *there was but one mainspring to all our thoughts and actions, and that was, the building of the Lord's house. I often wonder, when I hear brethren and sisters complain at the trifling inconveniences which they have to suffer in these days, and I think to myself that salvation is worth as much now as it was in the commencement of the work.*

Finally our beautiful temple that I had prayed over and many Saints sacrificed to build was completed. Often when the mobs were quiet, I would take walks and look at the Lord's house in the horizon. This brought unspeakable happiness to my soul.

More trouble came in the fall of 1836. The bank we had established went into distress, like many others across the country at that time, because *a large amount of money had been taken away by fraud.* This incident brought on many troubles that eventually caused us to flee for our lives to Far West, where a large branch of Saints were residing.

When we were being forced out of Kirtland, *I went to New Portage, and brought my husband to his family, and we all proceeded together on our journey, highly delighted to enjoy each other's society again, after so long a separation.* My sons, filled with the fever of the gospel, had many opportunities to preach along the way, but since this was not prudent for the circumstances they held off on spreading the word.

We frequently found ourselves in *disadvantageous circumstances,* which we pressed through anyway. *Sometimes we lay in our tents, through driving storms; at other times we were traveling on foot through marshes and quagmires. Once in particular, we lay all night exposed to the rain, which fell in torrents, so that when I arose in the morning, I found that my clothing was perfectly saturated with the rain,* which made it useless to *mend the matter by a change of dress, for the rain was still falling rapidly, and I wore my clothes in this situation, three days; in consequence of which I took a severe cold, so that when we arrived at the Mississippi river, I was unable to walk or sit up.* This caused my husband and family much concern not only about my condition but also over our daughter

Catherine who gave birth to her son Alvin in a negro hut we found along the way. My brave daughter grew ill from the weather conditions and the exhaustion of bringing a baby into this life. My worries over her grew so grave that Sophronia and her husband, McLerie, agreed to stay with Catherine and tend to her until she regained enough strength to continue the journey.

The rest of the family continued on to Huntsville, but our progress was slow *on account of a violent cough with which I was afflicted.* I began to be troubled over my condition and my lack of ability to tend to my daughter, grandson, and to help my other family members.

As the illness consumed me, draining me of my strength, and the mob's anger pressed against us, I knew that I must do something about my circumstances. *The next morning the family being absent, I seized the opportunity to make an effort to get far enough to pray without interruption.* To walk I had to struggle with sticks, but I pressed on, making my way to *reach a dense thicket. As soon as I sufficiently rested to speak with ease, I commenced calling upon the Lord, beseeching him to restore me to health, as well as my daughter Catharine, I urged every claim.* I stood out in the rain for three hours praying to have this alignment lifted from me and my daughter. As the drops fell upon me, I began to rehearse all the promised blessings that were given to the righteous *by the Scriptures.* I went over the covenants until at last I felt relieved *from every kind of pain; my cough left me, and I was well.* Grateful, I offered a prayer of thanks and set to tasks that needed to be done so we could continue with the journey.

Later that day Wilkins J. Salisbury, Catharine's husband, arrived in Huntsville and *informed us that Catharine was so much better, that, if she had a carriage to ride in, she could proceed on her journey.*

At Far West Joseph Jr. put us up in a tavern, *which he had recently purchased. Samuel had moved to a place called Marrowbone, Daviess County. William had moved thirty miles in another direction. We were all now quite comfortable.* Despite our dream for peace, more injustices, stress, and evil doing befell us. I will not speak of most of them except for one story that stands out in my mind. This event concerned the Saints' efforts to vote in Gallatin, Daviess County. The mob saw to it that they failed in this attempt. The mob's mischief did not stop there. They obtained the assistance of the *judge of the election, they wrote letters to all the adjoining counties, begging their assistance against the "Mormons." They stated that Joseph Smith had, himself, killed seven men at the election that day previous, and that the inhabitants had every reason to expect that he would collect his people together, as soon as possible, and murder all that did not belong to his Church. These letters were extensively circulated, and as widely believed.*

A few days later I was at my home enjoying some time with my son Joseph. He wanted to write a letter. *While he was thus engaged, I stepped to the door, and looking toward the prairie, I beheld a large company of armed men advancing towards the city, but, as I supposed it to be training day said nothing about it.* I watched them *until the main body came to a halt* in front of my home. My grasp on my apron tightened as I saw *the officers dismounting, eight of them came into the house. Thinking they had come for some refreshment, I offered them chairs, but they refused to be seated, and, placing themselves in a line across the floor, continued standing. I again requested them to sit, but they replied, "We do not choose to sit down; we have come here to kill Joe Smith and all the 'Mormons.'"*

It was not difficult to determine from their countenance that they meant what they said. I looked the officer straight in the eye, demanding to know why he would want to kill my son. When it became apparent that these men believed the lies that had been circulating about Joseph's behavior, I told them that their reports were false. Then I proceeded to say, "*Furthermore, if you should see him, you would not want to kill him.*"

"*There is not doubt that the report is perfectly correct,*" rejoined the officer; "*it came straight to us, and I believe it; and we were sent to kill the Prophet and all who believe in him, and I'll be d-d if I don't execute my orders.*"

"*I suppose,*" said I, "*you intend to kill me, with the rest?*"

"*Yes, we do,*" returned the officer.

"*Very well,*" I continued, "*I want you to act the gentleman about it, and do the job quick. Just shoot me down at once, then I shall be at rest; but I should not like to be murdered by inches.*"

"*There it is again,*" said he. "*You tell a 'Mormon' that you will kill him, and they will always tell you, 'that is nothing; if you kill us, we shall be happy.'*"

Joseph, just at this moment finished his letter, and, seeing that he was at liberty, I said, "Gentlemen, suffer me to make you acquainted with Joseph Smith, the Prophet." They stared at him as if he were a specter. He smiled, and stepping towards them he gave each of them his hand, in a manner which convinced them that he was neither a guilty criminal nor yet a hypocrite.

Joseph then sat down and explained to them the views, feelings, etc., of the Church, and what their course had been; besides the treatment which they had received from their enemies since the first. He also argued, that if any of the brethren had broken the law, they ought to be tried by the law, before anyone else was molested. After talking with them some time in this way, he said, "Mother, I believe I will go home now; Emma will be expecting me." *At this two of the men sprang to their feet, and declared that he should not go alone, as it would be unsafe—that they would go with him, in order to protect him.*

Joseph stopped and looked at the men with his gentle blue eyes. "I need to return to my wife," he finally said.

"We will go with you," one of the men offered.

"Yes, we will be your protection so you can return to your family."

These men were as good as their word. My son returned safely. The only way I can explain my calmness, Joseph's, and knowing what to do was our trust in God. God did not fail us. Miraculous events such as this occurred many times. This happens to be one that I remember well.

I will not write much about my Missouri days because it was a black time. There were problems from the start. That point in my life was like a nightmare. There was a constant element of worry, fear, and injustice. Our enemies called us "Mormons" and threatened us with violence to the point of trying to exterminate us. Mobs continually gathered together against us. My sons would try to form alliances with government officials who told them that our people would be safe, only to have them turn and betray us. The mobs would take away our hogs and cattle or shoot them for pleasure. They destroyed our peoples' crops. Many Saints died trying to secure food for their families. The mob would also enter into homes and steal the Saints most precious possessions including their money, bedding, and clothes. Many Saints were taken hostage in their towns and if they tried to leave, they were fired upon with cannons and rifles. We, as a people, were provoked. The mob would kidnap men, women, and children, whipping them and tying them to trees, hoping to provoke our anger so the mob could more easily destroy us. Thousands of Saints were driven from their homes, some without any shelter from the weather. During all this, my son, Joseph Jr., was faithful in petitioning the governor to stop these atrocities. We hoped that the government would do something in our favor.

Our hope turned out to out to be fruitless. The governor stated he would do nothing to help us in our plight. Instead he made it legal to "exterminate" the Mormons. This launched the evil men into a rage of killing, taking hundreds of people at Haun's Mill and other places.

My sons, Joseph and Hyrum, were lured into the enemy camp under the pretense of making a truce. My husband and I stood on the steps of our house and heard horrid yells come from the enemy camp. *Not knowing the cause, we supposed they were murdering him. Soon after the screaming commenced, five or six guns were discharged. At this, my husband, folding his arms tight across his heart, cried out, "Oh, my God! my God! they have killed my son! they have murdered him! and I must die, for I cannot live without him!"*

I had no word of consolation to give him, for my heart was broken within me—my agony was unutterable. I assisted him to bed, and he fell back upon it helpless as a child, for he had not strength to stand upon his feet. The evil noises continued for some time. The noise could not harm us any more though for we thought Joseph Jr. had died. This event so devastated my husband that he *was immediately taken sick, and never afterwards entirely recovered, yet he lived about two years, and was occasionally quite comfortable, and able to attend meetings.*

Later a messenger came to us and informed us that our sons were being taken to Far West and *if we were ever to see our sons alive we must go immediately to them, for they were in a wagon that would start in a few minutes for Independence, and in all probability they would never return alive.* My husband and I could not enjoy the relief of the news that our boys yet lived because of the pressing stress of not knowing if they were going to be taken shortly. Nevertheless, I would not miss the opportunity to have another correspondence with my sons. I hoped to have some last words with them and to touch them for at least one more time while on this earth. I wanted to strengthen them as much as I could with a mother's love. *Lucy and myself set out directly. My daughter and I went with great speed for fear that we would miss them. On coming within about a hundred yards of the wagon, we were compelled to stop,* because of the crowds. I did what I had done before when Caleb had taken my wagon on the way to Palmyra and left me stranded with my children—I appealed to the mercies of those around me. *"I am the mother of the Prophet; is there not a gentleman here, who will assist me to that wagon, that I may take a last look at my children, and speak to them once more before I die?" Upon this, one individual volunteered to make a pathway through the army, and we passed on, threatened with death at every step, till at length we arrived at the wagon.*

Grateful to come to the wagon holding my sons, I was much anxious to talk with them. The tall man I was with graciously talked with Hyrum and found that he was seated at the front of the wagon. He told my son that I requested that Hyrum reach his hand out that I might take a hold of it for *I was not allowed to see him; the cover was of strong cloth, and nailed down so close, that he could barely get his hand through.* Although my son did not speak to me, (I supposed that if he did he would have been killed) I could feel his love in our touch. His grip was tight and reassuring of his tender feelings for me. No sooner had we intertwined fingers than the mob ordered that I speak not a word or I would be shot. My daughter, shaking, clasped hands with her brother before we were prodded on.

The volunteer then took me and my daughter to the back of the wagon where Joseph was. The man spoke to him. *"Mr. Smith, your mother and sister are here, and wish to shake hands with you."* No sooner had this man spoken than Joseph's hand squeezed out from underneath the fabric. Both my daughter and I seized it and held his hand tight. There was no word spoken from him or us. I could not stand the silence any longer and cried, *"Joseph, do speak to your poor mother once more. I cannot bear to go till I hear your voice."*

"God bless you, mother!" he sobbed out.

Then a cry was raised, and the wagon dashed off, tearing him from us just as Lucy was pressing his hand to her lips, to bestow upon it a sister's last kiss—for he was then sentenced to be shot.

My daughter and I wrapped our arms around each other for support, tears staining our faces as we watched the wagon carrying our precious sons and brothers away from us. The pain that our house suffered after that incident was much. Emma and Mary Fielding were too much overcome to do more than succumb to their grief.

I gathered my grandchildren as a hen gathers her chicks and tried to comfort their breaking and fear-filled hearts. I told them about their fathers being in God's hands. The pressure to carry the burden of what happened and to lead my family to exercise faith rested heavy on me.

Having our sons imprisoned and ill-fed, and hearing of other Saints being driven from their homes, beaten, and raped became too much for my husband to endure. His health deteriorated quickly during that time.

Where much is given, much is required. I collected myself and began to remind my husband, my daughters-in-law, my grandchildren and other Saints of God's great mercies. I attended to the sick and afflicted and made myself useful in the Lord's hands. I also sought the Lord's guidance like I had done so many times before. I needed direction and after much prayer I was *filled with Spirit of God, and received the following by the gift of prophesy: "Let your heart be comforted concerning your children, they shall not be harmed by their enemies; and, in less than four years, Joseph shall speak before the judges and great men of the land, for his voice shall be heard in their councils. And in five years from this time he will have power over all his enemies."* This brought much comfort, which I immediately shared with the family who also were consoled in this reassurance. Many horrible troubles befell us as my sons were in Liberty jail and once again we were forced to flee for our lives and find a place to build up as our own.

Chapter 10

We had built up cities only to have them burned down and be chased out of town. At times our hearts grew weak trying to find the courage and the strength to build up another place we could rest our heads and call home. Joseph and Hyrum were still in jail when we were driven to Quincy, Illinois. While there we related our stories to the townspeople and they most graciously took us in. *Whilst we were sick, the ladies of Quincy sent us every delicacy which the city afforded; in fact, we were surrounded with the kindest of neighbors.* I have often prayed that those great people will be richly blessed in this life and in the afterlife for their service.

In the spring of 1839, Joseph and Hyrum made a purchase of a tract of land in Commerce. This town would later be renamed Nauvoo. There was much discouragement when the Saints saw the swampland for the first time. The mosquitoes that thrived there brought a horrible illness on most of the Saints.

Life on the frontier brings constant realities of death and survival. Death comes to our animals, plants, neighbors, and at times it comes after our children. Eventually it flirts with our own existence. Despite the fact that death was a frequent reality in our lives, we still felt the shock, pain, and sorrow when it struck home. The horror and anguish of losing a loved one still swells our hearts with unspeakable emotion that no human can actually put into words. And yet death, losing loved ones, is something that happens to everyone. Eventually all must leave this existence. so why are we so surprised when our gracious God calls us back?

I grow philosophical, perhaps as a shield from the torment that wracks me when I think about what I must write. How can I leave it out? Yet how can I even recognize it as fact by spilling it onto paper?

I will never truly capture the feelings of everyone affected; therefore I will blurt it out. The beginning of our sorrows came in 1840. We, my husband and I, had recently settled in our new home. Joseph Jr. saw to it that we had a home built with modern comforts. I saw the tenderness in Joseph Jr. as he went to so much trouble to see that we had our own dwelling instead of living with him and Emma. I was touched by my son's efforts and could see Alvin living through Joseph Jr. on this account. I was glad Alvin's goodness was being passed on to others who knew him and had partaken of his spirit.

Over the past several years, my dear husband had struggled with his health, with bouts of weakness and pain. The problem had progressed to the degree that medicine no longer had any effect or benefit for him. This distressed me greatly, being much concerned and pained at seeing my husband and the father of our children in such a condition. Due to the loss of many physical functions, he aged rapidly before us.

I began to notice a pattern. When sore trials befell his children or others in his family, Joseph seemed to lack the strength to fight his ailments, and his condition grew worse. For example, in the spring of 1839 when the land of Commerce had been purchased, most of our family moved there. Joseph and I lived in the attached part of Joseph Jr. and Emma's house.

That time period was hard on all the Saints in Commerce. The environment was harsh and many people came down with agues and bilious fever. Whole families became so ill that no one was able to continue on with daily life or even do things as simple as getting a drink of water. To our great sadness, we watched as the illness overcame our dear son Hyrum and all those in his family. Our daughter Lucy was also attacked by this illness.

Being much filled with anguish, I assisted my son Joseph and his wife Emma in bringing the sick people into their home and attending to their needs. We spent many days in prayer and performing the labors of a nurse. Our work was laid before us as more and more people fell victim to the disease. There were so many who were ill that beds were set up outside the home in tents, because the inside was already filled with the afflicted.

In the midst of all this, Joseph Jr. received a command from the Lord that he was to get his family in a position where he could leave once again. He had only recently returned from prison, where he had been sent because men had falsely accused him of breaking the law, which he did not do. He was to journey to the city of Washington, D.C. to address the President of the United States and also to speak to Congress about the plight of the Mormons and the treatment that had befallen the Saints.

The news that Joseph Jr. was to depart again pierced my heart, for I looked at Emma and all our work aiding the sick in our home. I felt her aching heart and strong desire to be with her husband. I studied my husband and the worry that filled him for our son and for what he was about to do, remembering well the trials he had already endured. Sometimes the awful memories of what had already happened were worse than the fear of what lay ahead. My husband and I prayed together often, me by his bedside, that the Lord would be with our son to guide and protect him, and help him as he suffered the same type of brutalities that some of the ancient apostles and prophets had to endure.

We were unable to express to each other what we felt through all this time, nor discuss the risk our children faced. Yet somehow we talked of the Lord and His goodness and His will. We knew whatever happened to us or to our children would be for our benefit. I tried with all my might to put my trust in the Lord with hopes that all the hardships that befell us were under His control. Joseph Jr. *began to feel the effects of the hardships which [he] had endured, and also the unhealthiness of the climate in which [he was] then situated. [He] came down with the agues and bilious fever.* One day Joseph rose off of the floor and began blessing people to be healed. He also received healing. Men gathered and went back and forth to the river, healing those with whom they came in contact.

After Joseph Jr. again left our sides, taking Sidney Rigdon, Elias Higbee, Dr. Foster, and Porter Rockwell with him, my husband fell gravely ill. It was as though when Joseph Jr. was near, he had strength. When Joseph Jr. was gone, the worry took over, chasing away any of the strength Joseph felt while in his son's presence.

My husband's illness had transformed him into a frail figure of a man, who began to be much wracked by coughs. He could not move out of the bed of his own will, but had to be assisted, which was humbling to him. My heart ached to see the shame in his eyes as he glanced away from us when he had to be moved. Most of the time he had such a shadow cast over his eyes that I wondered if he was not already drifting from us.

I inquired of the Lord if it was His will to take my husband from me. I was not alone in this thought because my husband also commented, "I worry I might go into the next life without you, Lucy. This would be a very hard burden on you. This is something that I do not wish for you to have to go through."

"*Rest that fear,*" I said. "That will not be the case, for it was *impressed upon my mind that, when you die, [you] would have children around [you].*"

Relief seemed to wash over him. "This is good," he said. "I feel a great desire to give a last blessing to Joseph when he returns. I feel he will need it."

Joseph's health took a turn for the better. By spring when the earth celebrated the newness of life, my husband celebrated a newness of health as he grew strong enough to walk a little and attend some meetings. This meant that not only was he at the meetings, taking in all that happened there, but he continued in his calling as the Church patriarch and gave blessings to others. It meant much to my husband that he could serve and render such blessings in other people's lives.

Meanwhile, Joseph Jr. immediately set to organizing this great city, building up homes, a university, schools, a theater. He also made efforts with the United States government to improve our conditions.

Sometimes when I reflected on the situation, I found myself overcome. I was amazed at the suffering the Saints were enduring. I was shocked at the hatred men had against the work and at how much the devil wanted to stop it. These reflections did not discourage me, but lifted me up to recognize the many miracles I was witnessing under God's hand.

As seasons passed in Nauvoo, the Saints were able to experience a peaceful time. I relished the sweet memories of times I was blessed to share with my family. I was often visiting my different children in their homes and saw grandchildren come into the world. The children often went sledding and skating in the winter and swam in the summer. We had good, fun times. We started again to build a temple. We all much looked forward to its completion. We knew we were building up Zion and were very pleased to be the Lord's instruments in doing so.

In March 1840, our Joseph Jr. returned to find his father had grown ill once more and was again confined to bed. But his health quickly returned and he was able to fulfill his wish of giving his son one more blessing, which he did.

News arrived that the persecutions of the Missouri Saints had increased again and the authorities of Illinois demanded that our sons Joseph and Hyrum return. The state claimed our boys were fugitives. There were warrants for their arrests, which meant our boys must flee again for their safety.

Although this news was of the greatest distressing manner, my worries were consumed with the welfare of my husband, who was coughing up blood and turning gray in color. Through various events that I will not write here, my boys were able to be at home to pay their father a visit, knowing their time with him was drawing to an end. My dear husband turned to speak to me first. I will not forget his words. They helped strengthen me for the rest of my life.

"Mother, do you not know that you are the mother of as great a family as ever lived upon the earth? The world loves its own, but it does not love us. It hates us because we are not of the world; therefore, all its malice, is poured out upon us, and they seek to take away our lives. When I look upon my children, and realize, that although they were raised up to do the Lord's work, yet they must pass through scenes of trouble and affliction as long as they live upon the earth; and I dread to leave them surrounded by enemies."

He had spoken the fear of my heart with those words. There was nothing I could do, nothing he could do, to protect our children from their trials. Hyrum must have sensed the truth and the unavoidable reality of this. He spoke to his father, asking, *"Father, if you are taken away, will you not intercede for us at the throne of grace, that our enemies may not have so much power over us?"*

Joseph, not yet being released from his Church calling, reached over to Hyrum's head and placed his hands on it to give him a father's blessing before he left this life. A clearness and strength came into my husband's voice as he spoke the words that God instructed him.

If truth be told, as a mother I wanted no challenges to come to my second boy, Hyrum. I had watched him go through much pain and the refiner's fire, but since that wish could not be, the knowledge that Hyrum would serve others, have peace, and be *firm as the pillars of heaven unto the end of [his] days,* was as much as any mother could hope. Joy filled my heart with the realization that my oldest living boy would not falter from the faith.

My husband took a rest before directing his words toward Joseph Jr. He smiled at him and said, *"Joseph, my son, you are called to a high and holy calling. You are even called to do the work of the Lord. Hold out faithful and you shall be blessed and your children after you. You shall even live to finish your work."*

Relief filled the room with this revelation. Overcome and weeping, our middle child, the Prophet of the Church, said, *"Oh! my father, shall I?"*

"Yes," he said. *"You shall live to lay out the plan of all the work which God has given you to do."*

This revelation filled the room with peace as all were anxious to see God's church, will, and law come forth. I don't know if my relief was more than my son's, knowing that he should live to complete what God had laid out before him. My husband also seemed surprised and pleased. But somewhere deep down I wondered if this blessing hinted that he would soon be taken from us.

After recovering from the emotion caused by this revelation, my husband turned to bless Samuel. In the blessing Joseph Sr. stated that God knew of Samuel's pain and the persecution he went through so privately. My son was known by God, being watched over and cared for by Him. I was impressed not only by the tender knowledge of God's workings in our lives, but also that yet another one of my sons had attained God's approval. Samuel had been declared faithful and clean. A mother could ask no more of any of her children.

William was next to receive a blessing from his father. My husband's voice had grown weaker, but his words were still powerful.

My boy, William, who had been called to be one of the Twelve Apostles and who had written accounts of the events before the Book of Mormon was published, was to continue on his path as a missionary. This seemed right. I was satisfied with the path of my William, who had worked so hard on the farm to keep it up while the older men traveled elsewhere to earn money for the family. While tilling the ground, courage and boldness must have entered his soul.

The courage he displayed when he stood against the mob that attacked our home, and the courage it took to declare the gospel in foreign lands, must be present in a faithful follower of Christ.

I watched my husband give the gifts of his blessings to his children, knowing this would be one of his last actions. He had worked his way through most of the boys, and after taking a rest and allowing me to give him water, which he sipped from a cup, he gave a blessing to Don Carlos, our last son.

Don Carlos was blessed that he would complete his mission. This was a great testimony to me as I listened, grateful that my children's lives would be preserved despite the constant threat against them from the dark side. Upon hearing the blessing that was bestowed on Don Carlos, I could not help but think about the integrity the boy showed at the mere age of fourteen, when he set out with his father in August, 1830, on a mission for Stockholm, St. Lawrence County, New York. My heart seemed to have been ripped out of my chest as I watched my two men leave. I was comforted by the knowledge that they would do God's work, and that even someone as young as Don Carlos could follow the instruction of the prophet, which might have been even more of a challenge, as the prophet was his older brother. But Don Carlos showed no ill intent and had been diligent in his service to the Lord up to this point.

My daughters were next to receive their father's blessings. Sophronia was first. My husband referred to Sophronia's early struggles, which brought back to my mind that event—the terror, the faith, the pleading with the Lord that both my husband and I had engaged in when she was so sick. We had begged the Lord to extend her life, and now, from his deathbed my husband promised her that she would live as long as she desired. The twists and contrast of events were ironic at times, but all these things showed God's goodness. Sophronia seemed satisfied with her blessing although tears streamed down her face. Her chin shook as she bravely gazed into the face of her father, whom she adored. It was as though she held back the grief that would explode in her heart once her father took his last breath.

At this time my husband needed to rest, so we respected his request with silence. I used this time to reflect upon seeing Joseph bless each of his children on his deathbed and how it must have been like this for the prophets of old, Abraham and Lehi and others who performed this sacred priesthood function. Lehi's and Abraham's words were preserved. I wanted to preserve the words of my husband. It was a startling interruption to our private prayers when he spoke again to bless Catherine.

He referred to the fact that my summer child had seen much trouble. She was born in a time where concerns pressed on us when we worried about providing for our ever-enlarging family and how to prepare for our elderly years that weren't far away. Not long after Catherine arrived in this world, typhoid fever struck our home. As she grew older, her early years were to be shaped by the challenges of persecutions. But this promised blessing that her suffering would end and she would have enjoyment in her life touched me deeply.

I was anxious to hear the promises and the words of the Lord for each of my children, yet with that desire came a sense of dread. I knew that once my husband progressed through the group he would be that much closer to his life's end. I wrung my hands and sighed a deep, soul-felt breath and listened, as now it was Lucy's turn.

What my husband said about Lucy seeing persecution throughout her whole life was true. I have wondered over the years what this would do to a person. How would it affect them? I understood that it would strengthen her as it had strengthened me. It would encourage a person to get on bent knees and seek the knowledge of God and His guidance. I have seen evidence of those characteristics in my child and myself. I was certain that without the obstacles I had been through in my earlier years and the things I saw my relatives experience, I would not have been able to withstand the trials that rained upon us in my later years. Lucy must have had the same kind of strength and endurance infused into her soul.

Yet Lucy would probably worry and fret over having a home and being driven from it. I prayed to God she would remember this day and the words her dying father had spoken—that she would no longer be driven to and fro. She would be required to put her trust and faith in God and not in the voice of past experience.

My husband's eyes turned back to me. We exchanged looks as we had done many times over the years. He wet his lips, breathing deeply, and said, *"Mother, do you know, that you are one of the most singular women in the world?"*

I struggled for words, being surprised by such a declaration. *"No,"* I said, *"I do not."*

He smiled the old familiar smile that made my heart reach out to him, drawing my affections toward him. *"Well, I do. You have brought up my children for me by the fireside, and when I was gone from home, you comforted them. You have brought up all my children, and could always comfort them when I could not. We have often wished that we might both die at the same time, but you must not desire to die when I do, for you must stay to comfort the children when I am gone. So do not mourn, but try to be comforted. Your last days shall be your best days, as to being driven, for you shall have more power over your enemies than you have had. Again I say, be comforted."*

Tears stained my face, but that did not bother me. I was much moved over the words my husband had spoken to me. We had many times voiced a desire to leave this existence hand-in-hand. I had much desired that exit, but as he spoke and reasoned with me that the children would need me to be here to comfort them, I knew he spoke correctly. That was my calling as a mother and I would not want to be denied the privilege of helping my children through sore affliction.

I reached out to my husband and squeezed his hand. He returned the gesture before saying, "*I can see and hear, as well as ever I could.*" He seemed amazed at this declaration and a light flittered across his face of a happiness I cannot yet find the words to describe. "*I see Alvin.*"

After forty-four years of marriage and building our lives together, I lost my husband to the great foe of death. His spirit soared to the kingdom up high where our oldest son, Alvin, waited. I could rest assured he was happy. *I then thought that the greatest grief which it was possible for me to feel, had fallen upon me in the death of my beloved husband. Although that portion of my life which lay before me, seemed to be a lonesome, trackless waste, yet I did not think that I could possibly find, in traveling over it, a sorrow more searching, or a calamity more dreadful, than the present.*

Eliza R. Snow was a dear friend of the family. Joseph Sr. loved the words she was able to write. As a gift to the family after Joseph went away from us, she penned the following poem. This expression brought much comfort.

ELEGY ON THE DEATH OF THE DEARLY BELOVED AND MUCH LAMENTED FATHER IN ISRAEL, JOSEPH SMITH, SENIOR, A PATRIARCH IN THE CHURCH OF JESUS CHRIST OF LATTER-DAY SAINTS, WHO DIED AT NAUVOO, SEPTEMBER 14, 1840

Zion's noblest sons are weeping
See her daughters bathed in tears,
Where the Patriarch is sleeping
Nature's sleep—the sleep of years.
Hushed is every note of gladness—
Every minstrel bows full low—
Every heart is tuned to sadness—
Every bosom feels the blow.

Zion's children loved him dearly;
Zion was his daily care:
That his loss is felt sincerely,
Thousand weeping Saints declare;
Thousands, who have shared his blessing,
Thousands who his service blessed,
By his faith and prayers suppressing
Evils which their lives opprest.

Faith and works, most sweetly blended,
Proved his steadfast heart sincere;
And the power of God attended
His official labors here;
Long he stemmed the powers of darkness,
Like an anchor in the flood:
Like an oak amid the tempest,
Bold and fearlessly he stood.

Years have witnessed his devotions,
By the love of God inspired,
When his spirit's pure emotions,
Were with holy ardor fired.
Oft he wept for suffering Zion—
All her sorrows were his own:
When she passed through grievous trials,
Her oppressions weighed him down.

Now he's gone, we'd not recall him
From a paradise of bliss,
Where no evil can befall him,
To a changing world like this.
His loved name will never perish,
Nor the Saints of God will cherish
The remembrance of the Just.
Faith's sweet voice of consolation,
Soothes our grief: his spirit's flown,
Upward to a holier station,

Nearer the celestial throne;
There to plead the cause of Zion,
In the council of the Just—
In the court the Saints rely on,
Pending causes to ADJUST.
Though his earthly part is sleeping,
Lowly 'neath the prairie sod;
Soon the grave will yield its keeping—
Yield to life the man of God.

When the heavens and earth are shaken,
When all things shall be restored—
When the trump of God shall waken
Those that sleep in Christ the Lord.

Miss E. R. Snow

Chapter 11

Death sometimes comes into a person's life like rainfall—light sprinkles that only hint at its existence or a thunderstorm that soaks and rattles your soul to the core. From the moment of my husband's passing, I felt that my family was caught in a dark thunderstorm that poured down upon us. Soon Joseph Jr. and Hyrum had to take flight for the safety of their lives.

Don Carlos, who towered above most men at six-foot-four, fell to the ravages of fever. My fair-haired somber son died at the age of twenty-six on August 7, 1841. His long hours spent working in an office basement, learning the craft of printing from Oliver Cowdery, led to his fatal sickness. I am amazed at what Don Carlos was able to accomplish in his short life. He married Agnes Coolbrith and they had three daughters. He became the editor of *Times and Seasons,* a member of the Nauvoo City Council, president of the high priests quorums in Kirtland and Nauvoo, brigadier general in the Nauvoo Legions, Lieutenant Colonel in the Hancock County Militia, and a member of the board of regents of the University of Nauvoo. His passing and the grief I saw in his widowed wife and fatherless children was hard to witness. Don Carlos' death struck me with such grief I thought I could not bear it. Little did I know what lay in store.

Joseph's and Hyrum's lives were sought once more by a mob consisting mostly of bitter apostates. My sons fled into hiding, but were asked by the Saints to come back and defend the town. When they returned to Nauvoo, they were arrested for treason on the morning of the twenty-fifth of June. For three days they remained prisoners with the company of Brother Richards, Taylor and Markham. The Governor left the prison to travel to Nauvoo. While he was gone, *he left a guard of eight of our bitterest enemies over the jail, and sixty more of the same character about a hundred yards distant. The men soon attacked the prison armed, painted black, red and yellow, and in ten minutes fled again, leaving my sons murdered and mangled corpses!*

When the shots were fired by a mob at Carthage, taking my sons Hyrum and Joseph from this life, I knew the greatest thunderstorm yet was upon me. How was a mother supposed to comprehend that the child she brought to earth, bore, fed, fought the fiery foe of disease for, taught, nourished, loved and comforted, could grow up to be an individual that would attract such hatred and disgust? It was difficult to believe men would seek my child out of thousands and cover his flesh with tar, poison his innards, thrust him into a heatless jail in the winter months and then, when their hate became so great, would not halt their pursuit until the blood of my child was spilled. How can a mother's mind suppose all this to happen, not once, but twice?

What great wrong did my Joseph Jr. do? Or my Hyrum? What evil did they commit that was so horrible that such treatment of them was justified? What did they do? My soul screamed. What did they do that I'm now left to bury my boys, their wives are left without spouses, and their young children are left fatherless?

How is a mother to endure the extreme agony of witnessing two of her heartsakes taken in one moment? How am I to understand how men's hearts could hate what I love and hold so precious?

What was I to do? Forsake God? Curse him and die? I say not. I would not. No, somehow, someway, in my old age I determined I must find a path to travel that would allow me to bless others as long as the Lord saw fit to grace me with life.

I had for a long time braced every nerve, roused every energy of my soul, and called upon God to strengthen me; but when I entered the room, and saw my murdered sons extended both at once before my eyes, and heard the sobs and groans of my family, and the cries of "Father! Husband! Brothers!" from the lips of their wives, children, brothers and sisters, it was too much, I sank back, crying to the Lord, in the agony of my soul, "My God, my God, why hast thou forsaken this family!" A voice replied, "I have taken them to myself, that they might have rest."

I was swallowed up in the depths of my afflictions and though my soul was filled with horror past imagination, yet I was dumb, until I arose again to contemplate the spectacle before me, Oh! at that moment how my mind flew through every scene of sorrow and distress which we had passed, together, in which they had shown the innocence and sympathy which filled their guileless hearts. As I looked upon their peaceful, smiling countenances, I seemed almost to hear them say, "Mother, weep not for us, we have overcome the world by love; we carried to them the gospel, that their souls might be saved; they slew us for our testimony, and thus placed us beyond their power; their ascendancy is for a moment, ours is an eternal triumph."

Others watched me as I grieved this loss. They sought me. "Mother Smith" they called me, wanting my strength, my guidance, my comfort in my darkest hour. This spiritual crisis was what my life had prepared me for. This was where God had guided me, preparing me for this pain, this torture. He cultivated my faithfulness through the many losses of loved ones, so I could stand strong at the time when I lost my husband and, in a few short months, three of my boys—two of them murdered in broad daylight as they stood helplessly trapped in Carthage jail; shot to death as they struggled to flee the poisonous anger that had consumed the mobbers' souls. Escape wasn't to be . . . not in mortality.

My heart burns now with another truth that I know as surely as I know they are dead—Jesus is the Christ. He lives so we will live again. In a short time I will see my husband, Alvin, Don Carlos, Hyrum and Joseph again. Glorious will be our reunion. Great shall be my joy because of the infinite power of the Atonement and its saving property.

At my sons' deaths, faithful Eliza R. Snow again labored with her pen to gift the family with a beautiful portrait capturing the essence of our loved ones. These poems were much loved by the Saints who read them oft as they struggled to deal with their grief.

Lines Written on the Death of Gen. Don Carlos Smith

> *"Thy shaft flew thrice, and thrice my peace was slain."*
> *The insatiate archer, Death, once more*
> *Has bathed his shaft in human gore;*
> *The pale-faced monarch's crimsoned bow,*
> *Once more has laid a good man low.*

If tears of love could ever save
A noble victim from the grave;
If strong affection e'er had power
To rescue in the dying hour;
If kindred sympathy could hold
A jewel in its sacred fold;
If friendship could produce a charm,
The heartless tyrant to disarm;
If wide-acknowledge worth could be
A screen from mortal destiny;
If pure integrity of heart
Could baffle death's malignant dart;
If usefulness and noble zeal,
Devotedness to Zion's weal,
A conduct graced with purposed aim,
A reputation free from blame,
Could save a mortal from the tomb,
And stamp with an eternal bloom;
He never could have bowed to death,
Or yielded up his mortal breath.

Ours is the sorrow, ours the loss,
For, through the triumphs of the Cross,
His noble part, by death set free,
On wings of immortality,
Tracing the steps the Savior trod,
Has reached the Paradise of God.

There he rejoins the ransomed choir,
There, there he hails his noble sire,
A patriarch of these latter-days,
Whose goodness memory loves to trace
With reverence, gratitude, and love;
He left us for the courts above.

There with the spirits of the just,
Where Zion's welfare is discussed,
Once more their efforts to combine
In Zion's cause. —And shall we mourn
For those who have been upwards borne!
And shall the Legion's sorrow flow,
As if a Chieftain were laid low,
Who threw his frail escutcheon by,
To join the Legion formed on high?
Yes, mourn. —The loss is great to earth,
A loss of high exalted worth.

Miss E. R. Snow.

The Assisination of Joseph and Hyrum Smith, First Presidents of the Church of Jesus Christ of Latter-day Saints, Who Were Massacred by a Mob in Carthage, Hancock County, Ill. on June 27, 1844

Ye heavens attend! Let all the earth give ear!
Let Gods and Seraphs, men and angels hear—
The worlds on high—the universe shall know
What awful scenes are acted here below!
Had Nature's self a heart, her heart would bleed,
For never, since the Son of God was slain,
Had blood so noble flowed from human vein,
As that which now, on God, for vengeance calls
From "Freedom's ground"—from Carthage prison walls!

Oh! Illinois! thy soil has drunk the blood
Of Prophets, martyred for the truth of God.
Once loved America! What can atone
For the pure blood of innocence thou'st sown?
Were all thy streams in teary torrents shed
To mourn the fate of those illustrious dead,
How vain the tribute, for the noblest worth
That graced thy surface, O degraded earth!
Oh! Wretched murd'rers! fierce for human blood!
You've slain the Prophets of the living God,

Who've borne oppression from their early youth,
To plant on earth the principles of truth.

Shades of our patriotic fathers! Can it be?
Beneath your blood-stained flag of liberty!
The firm supporters of our country's cause
Are butchered, while submissive to her laws!
Yes, blameless men, defamed by hellish lies,
Have thus been offer'd as a sacrifice
T'appease the ragings of a brutish clan,
That has defied the laws of God and man!

'Twas not for crime or guilt of theirs they fell;
Against the laws they never did rebel.
True to their country, yet her plighted fate
Has proved an instrument of cruel death!
Where are thy far-famed laws, Columbia, where
Thy boasted freedom—thy protecting care?
Is this a land of rights? Stern FACTS shall say,
If legal justice here maintains its sway,
The official powers of state are sheer pretense,
When they're exerted in the Saints' defense.

Great men have fallen, and mighty men have died;
Nations have mourned their fav'rites and their pride;
But two, so wise, so virtuous, great, and good,

Before on earth, at once, have never stood
Since the creation. Men whom God ordained
To publish truth where error long had reigned,
Of whom the world itself unworthy proved.
It knew them not, but men with hatred moved,
And with infernal spirits have combined
Against the best, the noblest, of mankind.

Oh! persecution! Shall thy purple hand
Spread utter destruction through the land?
Shall freedom's banner be no more unfurled?
Has peace, indeed, been taken from the world?

Thou God of Jacob, in this trying hour,
Help us to trust in thy Almighty power;
Support thy Saints beneath this awful stroke,
Make bare thine arm to break oppression's yoke.
We mourn thy Prophet, from whose lips have flowed
The words of life thy Spirit has bestowed;
A depth of thought no human art could reach,
From time to time rolled in sublimest speech,
From the celestial fountain, through his mind,
To purify and elevate mankind.
The rich intelligence by him brought forth,
Is like the sunbeam spreading o'er the earth.

Now Zion mourns, she mourns an earthy head;
The Prophet and the Patriarch are dead!
The blackest deed that men or devils know,
Since Calvary's scene, has laid the brothers low.
One in their life, and one in death—they proved
How strong their friendship—how they truly loved.
True to their mission, until death they stood,
Then sealed their testimony with their blood.
All hearts with sorrow bleed, and every eye
Is bathed in tears—each bosom heaves a sigh—
Heart-broken widows' agonizing groans
Are mingled with the helpless orphans' moans!

Ye Saints! be still, and know that God is just,
With steadfast purpose in his promise trust.
Girded with sackcloth, own his mighty hand,
And wait his judgments on this guilty land!
The noble martyrs now have gone to move
The cause of Zion in the courts above.

Miss E. R. Snow

Chapter 12

While viewing the bodies of Joseph and Hyrum, I became so overcome with emotion that I retired to my room for a visit with Samuel. He had been discovered by the mob when he tried to recover the bodies of his dead brothers. The mob attempted to number him among the dead, but he escaped, leading them on a chase for over two hours, my dear boy fleeing for his life.

While I was alone in my room, overcome with grief, he came to my side and said, "*Mother, I have had a dreadful distress in my side ever since I was chased by the mob, and I think I have received some injury which is going to make me sick.*"

I examined my son most carefully. He had not been able to sit up nor had he been able to rest from the great shock that had come upon us with both his brothers gone and the attempt on his own life. *In a short time Samuel, who continued unwell, was confined to his bed, and lingering till the thirtieth of July, his spirit forsook its earthly tabernacle, and went to join his brothers, and the ancient martyrs, in the Paradise of God.* Samuel was every bit as much a martyr as Joseph and Hyrum, dying for the cause. His sickness and ultimate demise were a direct result of the mob at Carthage.

I thought when my husband had been taken from me that it would be the height of my misery. I had been mistaken. It is great wisdom that we do not know the end from the beginning. The knowledge of such a happening I could not have borne. Now the knowledge is within my soul, my thoughts, my existence and yet I cannot comprehend.

I hold fast to the dying blessings my husband gave as a parting gift. Could he have known how much I would cleave to his words, his truths? Two of my children, William and Sophronia, were promised life for as long as they desired it. Joseph and Hyrum were promised that their missions would be completed before they were taken. There is comfort in that. My girls were promised happiness in their lives. I cling to that. I want to live to see my four remaining children happy and enjoying the life that my other children have been denied. Lord, have mercy on me for my sorrow and anguish. Continue to carry me until it is my time to greet Thee.

Many travelers come to visit me. I live in Nauvoo with Emma in the home she shared with Joseph. My dear Emma has suffered much. *I have never seen a woman in my life, who would endure every species of fatigue and hardship, from month to month, and from year to year, with that unflinching courage, zeal, and patience, which she has ever done; for I know that which she has had to endure—she has been tossed upon the ocean of uncertainty—she has breasted the storms of persecution, and buffeted the rage of men and devils, which would have borne down almost any other woman.* Emma never believed that Joseph would be taken from her. I did not, either. Now that Joseph only remains in memories, her heart is forever broken.

Hyrum's wife, Mary Fielding, of English stock, bore up well under the pressure and did not express much about losing her husband. She bravely ventured out on the trek west with her young children around her.

I often play with my grandchildren, teaching them about their heritage, and more importantly, about the gospel and the role God can play in their lives. When I am not with my grandchildren or aiding Emma with sewing or cooking, I entertain visitors. My visitors range from Brother Brigham Young and Brother Heber C. Kimball, to Brother Wilford Woodruff, who addresses me as "Old Mother" and "Prophetess." Wilford gave me a blessing saying, "When thou are called to depart thou canst lie down in peace having seen the salvation of God, in laying an everlasting foundation for the deliverance of Israel through the instrumentality of thy sons." Wilford continued, "Thou hast lived and stood to see the fall of thy sons by the rage of gentile hands. And like an impenetrable rock in the midst of the mighty deep thou hast remained unmoved until God has given thou the desires of thy heart in seeing the keys of the Kingdom of God held in the hands of thy Posterity so planted in the earth that they shall never be taken from it until he reigns whose right it is to reign."[13]

As I live with Emma, I have found much significance in relics of the past—so much so that I have created a small museum in our home as a way to show the curious part of Mormonism, to reveal to the believers their roots, and to guide the nonbelievers with an introduction to the truth. Many come and ask about the days past. I have collected Church magazines, newspapers, pamphlets, books, historical artifacts, and antiques.

I welcome visitors' questions. I want the world to remember the sacrifice of so many hundreds of people who were instruments of God in bringing the truth back into this world. May this book serve as an added testimony to that of others, that Jesus is the Christ. He died on the cross for you and me. I testify that the truth of this and many other great principles and doctrines can be found in the pages of the Book of Mormon.

I love the Book of Mormon and hope to spend the rest of my days testifying of its truthfulness. The Lord of us all has at last answered my prayers regarding religion and how to practice it. I am on fire with the truth and I fear not to speak of it to everyone I encounter. It is my hope that my offering on the Resurrection Day will be found to be enough. I *bid farewell, until I shall appear before Him who is the judge of both quick and dead; to whom I solemnly appeal in the name of Jesus Christ, Amen.*

The Venerable Lucy Smith

The aged, venerated, much belov'd
Mother in Zion, and the mother of
The greatest men this generation had
To boast, One, only one, of all her sons
Survives—the others sleep the sleep of death!
The great anointed seer and prophet, she
Has nurs'd upon her bosom and has watch'd
In helpless, cradled infancy: her heart
With deep solicitude had often yearn'd
Over his tender childhood, ere the God
Of heav'n reveal'd the glorious purpose which
Was pre-determined in the courts above,
Should be accompli[s]h'd in the present age:
But when she realiz'd the Lord had call'd
Him in his youth and inexperience to
Re-introduce the "ancient order" and
Confront the prejudices of the world;
The throbbings of her breast, none can describe;
And she can tell a tale that none besides
Can tell.

She's suffer'd much and much she had
Enjoy'd. I oft have sat beside her and
Have listen'd with sweet admiration to

Her strains of heav'nly eloquence while she
Describ'd the glories that are soon to be
Reveal'd.

She's witness'd change succeeding change
Roll up the tide of revolution till
Its heaving waves accumulating seem
About to burst and overwhelm the world!
The standard of our country, she has seen
Rising in glorious majesty, and wave
Its fam'd, unrival'd banner gracefully,
Till other hands than those that rear'd it, sapp'd
Its broad foundation, and its ensign marr'd—
Tott'ring and tremulous it now appears
Ready to fall and in its fall to make
The most tremendous crash the civil world
Has ever known!

She's seen the church of God
Start into being and extend itself
From shore to shore and plant its footsteps on
The Islands of the sea.
She once beheld
Her lord, her consort dragg'd to prison while
With tears and supplicating words, she plead
His innocence, and begg'd for his release.

"Commit the Book of Mormon to the flames"
Replied the "officer of justice" and
Your husband shall be liberated:" But
Her noble spirit scorn'd to purchase his
Release, on terms so base! at such a price!
She lov'd the truth and fear'd the God of heav'n.
She's seen her children driv'n from place to place
And hunted like the mountain deer. She's stood
Beside the death bed of her noble lord
Who, ere the lamp of life became extinct,
Like ancient Jason, call'd his children round
And bless'd them one by one.
I knew him well,
For he was Zion's first great Patriarch;
And from his lips I've felt the sacred pow'r
Of blessing on my head. But he has gone,
And she in lonely widowhood remains!
She's follow'd to the grave, five noble sons!
She stood beside the bleeding forms of those
Great brother-martyrs of the latter-day.
Ah! think of her, ye tender mothers, when
Her feeble, tott'ring frame that bow'd beneath
The weight of years and life's infirmities,
Accumulated by the toils and cares,
Anxieties and oft heart-rending griefs:
Stood o'er her murder'd sons! She laid her hand

Upon their marble foreheads, while the blood
Was freely gushing from their purple wounds!
And yet she lives, and yet bears witness to
The truth for which they fell a sacrifice.

Yes, venerable Lady, thou shalt live
While life to thee shall be a blessing. Thou
Art dear to ev'ry faithful saint. Thousands
Already bless thee—millions yet to come
Will venerate thy name and speak thy praise.

Miss Eliza R. Snow

Afterword

The years after her sons' murders were not easy for Lucy. She was overcome with grief from the many misfortunes which were pressed upon her. To all who visited her, she would recount the hardships her family had endured. Brigham Young offered help from the Church for the wagon and supplies to go westward with the Saints. Lucy publicly declared she planned on going. This resulted in a joyous outcry, for she was much loved. But problems arose with Lucy's health and, more importantly, she became increasingly concerned about Emma, who suffered greatly from her husband's death. In the end, Lucy chose to remain behind although many of her beloved friends were going westward. Lucy longed to be with the Saints but felt that she should stay behind to be of assistance to her pregnant daughter-in-law and grandchildren. Lucy was actively involved in the last-minute work done in the Nauvoo Temple before the Saints departed. It brought her joy to see the temple be used around the clock as Brigham Young worked to get as many as possible endowed and sealed before crossing the plains.

Lucy moved frequently and lived with anyone who would provide for her. This continued until at last she settled with Emma and her new husband, Lewis Bidamon, who was reportedly very kind to Lucy. Lewis made her a wheelchair in which she sat, having her grandchildren push her through the garden and around the house.

Lucy Mack Smith died May 14, 1856 at the age of 81. She will be known forever as "Mother Smith," the prophetess and mother of the Prophet Joseph Smith Junior. Her sacrifice and faith are monuments to the causes she passionately fought for and lived embracing.

Notes

1. Solomon Mack, *Narrative,* Vermont, Windsor, 1810, 35–36.

2. Solomon Mack, *Narrative,* Vermont, Windsor, 1810, 41.

3. Solomon Mack, *Narrative,* Vermont, Windsor, 1810, 41.

4. Solomon Mack, *Narrative,* Vermont, Windsor, 1810, 11.

5. Solomon Mack, *Narrative,* Vermont, Windsor, 1810, 11–12.

6. Solomon Mack, *Narrative,* Vermont, Windsor, 1810, 17.

7. Solomon Mack, *Narrative,* Vermont, Windsor, 1810, 15–16.

8. Solomon Mack, *Narrative,* Vermont, Windsor, 1810, 8.

9. Solomon Mack, *Narrative,* Vermont, Windsor, 1810, 16–17.

10. Solomon Mack, *Narrative,* Vermont, Windsor, 1810, 16–17.

11. Joseph Smith History 1:20

12. Joseph Smith History 1:20

13. Ed. Lavina Fielding Anderson, *Lucy's Book: A Critical Edition of Lucy Mack Smith's Family Memoir,* 780.

References

Anderson, Lavina Fielding, ed. *Lucy's Book: A Critical Edition of Lucy Mack Smith's Family Memoir.* Salt Lake City: Signature Books, 2001.

Anderson, Mary Audentia Smith. *Ancestry and Posterity of Joseph Smith and Emma Hale.* Independence, Missouri: Herald House Publing, 1929.

Anderson, Richard Lloyd. *Joseph Smith's New England Heritage: Influences of Grandfathers Solomon Mack and Asael Smith.* Salt Lake City: Deseret Book, 1971.

Arrington, Leonard J, and Madsen, Susan Arrington, and Jones, Emily Madsen. *Mothers of the Prophets.* Salt Lake City: Bookcraft, 2001.

Bushman, Richard L. *Joseph Smith and the Beginnings of Mormonism.* Urbana and Chicago: University of Illinois Press, 1984.

Cumming, John and Audrey. *The Pilgrimage of Temperance Mack.* Mount Pleasant, Michigan, 1967.

Evans, John Henry. *Joseph Smith: An American Prophet*. New York: Macmillan, 1933.

Gibbons, Francis M. *Joseph Smith, Martyr, Prophet of God*. Salt Lake City: Deseret Book, 1977.

Hill, Donna. *Joseph Smith the First Mormon*. New York: Doubleday, 1977.

Mack, Solomon. *Narrative*. Vermont, Windsor, 1810.

Nibley, Preston. *Joseph Smith the Prophet*. Salt Lake City: Deseret News Press, 1944.

Smith, Lucy Mack. *Biographical Sketches of Joseph Smith the Prophet and His Progenitors for Many Generations*. Liverpool, England, 1853.

Tullidge, Edward W. *Life of Joseph the Prophet*. Plano, Illinois: Board of Publication of the Reorganized Church of Jesus Christ of Latter Day Saints, 1880.